Martin Miles has pr
a founder member of the Society of Homœopaths, and served as its first Chairperson. In 1977 he was co-founder of the College of Homœopathy in London, the first teaching institution for lay practitioners to be founded in this country.

Martin teaches and runs a busy practice in South London where he lives with his wife and two children.

Homœopathy and Human Evolution

Martin Miles

Winter Press
50 Rockbourne Road
London SE23 2DD

First published by Winter Press in 1992

ISBN 1 874581 00 2

Author photograph by Christopher Schwarz
Cover picture "The Reunion of the Soul and the Body"
by William Blake
Artwork by Neal's Yard Desk Top Publishing Studio
Printed in Great Britain by Biddles of Guildford, Surrey

CONTENTS

PREFACE

The origins of this book go back to teachings received by myself some eighteen years ago, and probably many times before that. The teaching itself is as old as humanity and I make no personal claim to it. It has been adapted to the needs of the people of this day and generation.

In the early 1970s I met Dr Thomas Maughan, who practiced homœopathy, and ran a small group in South London to which he taught a number of subjects including homœopathy. I attended every medical class, and missed few others, noting everything he said. It became my privilege to spend much time with Thomas, often receiving complex teachings while driving him around in a car at the very high speed he insisted upon. These teachings I had to remember and copy down later. What I forgot is what the locust ate.

At that time, homœopathy was largely unknown in this country. Those practising it kept a low profile, providing only for their small groups of patients and followers. It had lapsed into a deep slumber of approximately two generations. Most people had become bewitched by stories of wonder drugs, antibiotics, vaccines and other propaganda put out by the medical profession and the drug companies making vast profit by spoon-feeding misinformation to people. Before this time, during the last century and the early part of this one, homœopathy had been quite widely practiced. Now it was time for a renaissance.

At Thomas's death in 1976 the torch was passed on. A number of colleagues and myself from Thomas's group got together with a similar group from North London and the Society of Homœopaths was born, with something like twelve members. Soon after this Robert Davidson and I started the London College of Homœopathy, the first college of its kind, with a first year class of thirty people.

The rapid growth of homœopathy in the past two decades is

testimony to the need of the time. There are tides in the affairs of humanity and if these are followed then much energy, goodness and abundance is supplied.

This book is an attempt to unveil homœopathy as an evolutionary tool for the development of humanity in our new age. Its power, and far reaching implications are much greater than are generally realised. It is important therefore that we develop it for those who are in need now, and for those who will practice in the future with a far greater understanding than ours. Clinging to its original precepts to the exclusion of other knowledge will create a dead religion, becoming ever more meaningless and less effective.

Do not be afraid. Go out and be creative practitioners, for when we freely go with what is meant to be, the spirit of the age is with us.

FOREWORD

Martin Miles has been a practising homœopath and teacher of homœopathy for the past eighteen years. He is a renowned and respected homœopath with a wealth of experience gained from his busy full-time practice.

Martin has been guided and inspired in the writing of this book, and much of the information written herein has been received by those teaching us on the higher levels and especially by his teachers.

It is becoming evident as we move into the New Age that we, as homœopaths, have to change to move with the age. We need to become more open minded and more enlightened. In many cases our understanding and our prescribing has to shift to meet the changing times and the general poor state of our patients' health these days.

The consciousness of us all – as individuals, as a nation and that of the whole world – is undergoing a massive positive change on every level, physical, emotional, mental and spiritual. We must learn to follow our individual path, use our individual gifts, follow our heart and listen to the teacher within.

As homœopaths we must also remember that we are as individual as are our patients, and we must therefore use our individual gifts within our healing mission and move forwards in trust and faith; always remembering that all healing ultimately comes from God. We are just instrumental in moving our patients towards their own inner enlightenment, enabling them to see and follow their own paths. We learn from each experience according to our own needs in order to fulfil our own karma, and we therefore attract our patients accordingly so that we may also learn from them.

Homœopathy is an inner experience, taking us to new levels of understanding and consciousness. Listen to its higher messages. Homœopathy becomes a way of life, or should do, if you are following a path in your life. Homœopathy is not just a passing phase, and this message needs to be conveyed to those patients who are capable of understanding, as they are educated so they move on. The healing process cannot be hurried, the more gently and slowly it is allowed to happen, the easier it becomes. Many patients will change without realising it, without trauma.

Many patients that come to us are frightened and lost, and cannot see a way forward. They present with symptoms that have little to do with why they have come. Through homœopathy, we have the ability to remove the fear and help our patients to find themselves. We all need to be open to the higher reasons for prescribing.

Martin has 'listened' and written this book as he was inspired. Some of the receivings you may not understand at the present, but when you are ready to 'hear', it will be made apparent to you. Within the following pages are many messages for you, if you can open your hearts and listen.

Let reading these pages uplift you and help you to open your heart and mind to a higher level of understanding and to increase your level of consciousness. May God bless you all in your healing mission.

Janice Micallef
Bexley, Kent
April 1992

ACKNOWLEDGMENTS

Books are usually the fruits of group endeavour and this is no exception. Without the roots working in the dark earth, we would not have the flower. I would like to extend my thanks to all those who have made this book possible and especially to the following.

Firstly, Janice Micallef, for encouraging me to write this book and for her support throughout. To my editor and publisher Susan Curtis, who is so much a part of the spirit of it all, ensuring that the ideas retain their integrity. To Sylvia Treacher, for typing the manuscript and whose friendship and support are perennial. To my wife Pam, for putting up with my need to get it done. Also to Peter Firebrace, Colin Winter, David Loxley and Jennifer Maughan. To all the unseen guides and companions, who labour in the spirit of love and goodwill and give of themselves without price. Finally, to the Eagle Man, to whom so much is owed by so many without them knowing it, and from whom much of this work has been received.

Woe unto you conventionalists for you took away the key of the sacred science and would not go in. And those who were about to go in you prevented.

The cure of the part should not be attempted without treatment of the whole. No attempt should be made to cure the body without the soul. If the head and the body are to be healthy you must begin by curing the mind... for this is the great error of our day in the treatment of the human body, that physicians first separate the soul from the body.

Plato – THE REPUBLIC 382BC

INTRODUCTION

It is intended that the ideas contained within this book will provide the homœopathic prescriber and the interested reader with a greater understanding of the true potential of homœopathy as a tool to cure disease, create health and as an instrument for the evolution of humanity through time and space towards our ultimate goal. You are not expected to accept what is written without thought or question, without trial and result, for to do so is to be too passive. Neither, it is hoped, will you cast aside the contents without due consideration. It is easy to become ensnared by one's own prejudices, rejecting something new because it does not fit into the present habits of thought.

I would urge every aspiring homœopath to take the ideas, apply the power of your mind, relate them to what you already know. Do not draw quick conclusions, or make judgements, but store away any ideas you may have in the pigeon holes of the mind, so that one day when enough information is collated a new idea may be born.

> "Hold out your hand, take the idea and hold it fast, until the fruits of your endeavour bring forth riches in knowledge and understanding, so that in knowing you might also become."

The seasoned homœopathic prescriber knows that homœopathy works, he sees the results every day in his practice. He has no need for so-called scientific 'proof', sceptically conducted by those who have a vested interest in a negative outcome. As is ever the case, knowledge is received in the act of participating in the great drama of life itself, for she is the greatest teacher of all; the act of living is the process of knowing and the metamorphosis of becoming. True knowledge is not found in laboratories or by the experiments of material science conducted by those who stand on the touchline, but by those who play the game on the field.

The well-being and general condition of the physical body is often neglected by those interested in New Age psychology. Yet the physical vehicle is the temple of an indwelling spirit, this outward cloak being an exact reflection of the being who inhabits it. The disease found in the physical body tells us much about the person. No great spirit chooses for its vehicle a form so dense and disease-ridden as to deny it expression. Therefore, it is of great importance to heal and purify the instrument which your spirit has chosen, so that both may work as one, having no variance of will.

Life is a mirror, we project onto the world what we are, and the world reflects it back at us. The structure of our lives - our jobs, the partners we have, the cars we drive and the clothes we wear - is an expression of our inner being, manifesting in the world. By return, the world reflects our own qualities back at ourself; and the physical body reflects its condition back up again to the higher vehicles, contributing to our well-being or creating morbid deviations of purpose and expression.

If idle speculation and intellectual time-wasting were our purpose then we would be mind with no physical body, but the physical is the vehicle of action and it is in this field that we learn and become. To that extent the physical body is of some importance, and yet ultimately it is of no importance. The physical body grows old and dies at the point we call death, while we are left to proceed on our journey, to the next stage of our development.

So we must put our learning into practice, receive our results with goodwill and an open mind, and if the ideas work, use them; if they do not, then put them aside and seek our result through a different working hypothesis.

> "Hold that point of pure aspiration, and in so doing know that man is not just a piece of mobile protoplasm but is indeed a spiritual integrity."

CHAPTER 1

Karma

"Act because action is your duty and your karma."

In short, karma is the law of cause and effect. This is easy to understand: on putting your hand into the fire it gets burnt. Karma is the scales of perfect justice, it runs through the whole of creation and none are exempt.

There is long term and short term karma, and it traverses from one incarnation to the next. Throughout creation every cause has an effect, and every effect has a cause. In bumbling though our daily lives it is possible for some of us to identify the results of some of our actions. Most often, however, we hotly deny the results as our own, and quickly blame another for the painful consequences. This action is unfortunate as it means the recipient is not likely to learn from his experience. To avoid bad results careful thought and planning are required in our actions.

In order to learn about and improve our karma, two human qualities are required, they are memory and consciousness.

Memory

The average memory rarely lasts longer than two weeks, and many cannot even manage yesterday or the previous paragraph of this book. Memory depends on two things, firstly, on being conscious in the moment. In other words, those who are dreaming or dwelling in the past or future are not in the now, or present tense. In so doing they do not consciously register that which they will be called upon to remember at a later date. Secondly, memory relies upon access to the memory banks or association areas. Homœopathy is of infinite value in improving both of these processes.

How can an individual with a poor memory identify the reaction to his action? Indeed, how can he know it to be a reaction?

He may lament his karma if he has heard of such, but he will be unable to gain anything further. Who can remember what they were doing on this date a year ago, or ten years ago? As for past incarnations, it is not a surprise that this reality is doubted, because who can remember them? And yet, both good and bad results spill over into this life as the consequences of deeds done in past lives. Once this idea is fully grasped, people will take much more care over their choice of activity.

There is one more aspect of memory to be borne in mind. If you stir up the murky waters of your emotions the memory will be destroyed. Such activity clouds the mind and thought and memory fades. Homœopathic practitioners may observe this amongst their patients. That is to say, as long as they do not indulge in it too much themselves, for being so involved they would fail to recognise it in another.

Will the reader have concentrated sufficiently on what is read in order to recall it at a later date? Will the homœopathic practitioner be sufficiently in the present tense to assimilate and remember the very substance of her patient?

Consciousness

Consciousness is that vital ingredient that humanity has and which the animal and vegetable kingdoms do not have. It is awareness, and it extends to all that which we experience both inside and outside of ourselves.

We may be conscious of everything that we see and feel, but we were also conscious once of something else. Before our present incarnation the all-enduring spirit laid down the rough outlines of the path that we would travel. This will have been long forgotten by most of us.

The spirit's descent and crucifixion upon the cross of matter usually amounts to being plunged into the overwhelming darkness of the earthly life. The contact with the spirit is lost, and many are drowned in the sea of materialism, unaware of why they came here in the first place. They follow a lifestyle they were not intended to and the personality and little ego dictate the worldly pursuit of ambition, avarice and power over others. The spirit though, is well aware of what it ultimately wants, and let it be said now that the spirit will have its way, however long it may take.

This is how karma is enacted; in dragging back the individual who has gone astray, to his true purpose in life. It works by making his life uncomfortable, in fact, downright painful and chaotic, until the pain is too great for him to continue and he decides on a course of action which will be more suitable for him. Thus do we return to what we should have been doing in the first place. This is a very sensible and efficient mechanism when one is aware of it. The link is consciousness. Had the man the consciousness to know enough about himself and his true line of activity, the painful experience would not have been necessary.

When we have developed consciousness sufficiently, man will no longer require karma to keep us to our purpose. The trends that flow through our lives are often karmic. When we say that someone is lucky because a certain situation tends to repeat itself in their lives, for example, they continually find a harmonious environment to live in, this is karma in action. The same is true when we say that someone is unlucky for continually having bad experiences. In reality, there are no such things as luck, coincidence or victims. They do not exist except in language as a product of misunderstanding.

Our ability to choose (free will) is limited by karma. This is because we must primarily learn to serve the spirit. As we begin to more fully serve the spirit our life falls into a state of greater harmony and happiness. We must learn to perceive our purpose in life – the purpose of our unfolding spirit. Instead we spend our lives chasing trivia. The first step to finding our purpose is to concentrate on the job in hand, the present tense, because that is where you are now, and is the consequence of what one is.

Karma and Homœopathy

What does all this have to do with homœopathy and the homœopath/patient relationship? Broadly speaking, there are three aspects of the patient to be examined by the homœopath. These are the past, the present and the future.

We are taught in homœopathy to take down a detailed case

history. This is most important for it reveals the patterns of the past, the long-term habits of the patient and their effect upon the present condition. We are the result of all that we have been in the past. Our knowledge of this is only limited by our ability to perceive and understand it. When our knowing is greater we can see back through incarnations into the patient's past. The patient drags with him the dross of the past, the results of past errors and wrong doings, and that which he no longer needs. To the homœopath this is presented in the case history as disease, trauma, suppression, surgery, vaccination, accident, attitude, etc., and possibly the deepest of all as miasmatic disease.

It is miasmatic disease which constitutes by far the greater part of the disease process that so threatens the integrity of humanity. These diseases, as described originally by Samuel Hahnemann, are the venereal diseases and one other, which is basically leprosy and its successive mutations through the generations.

The consequences of these disease processes when recognised (and that is only by a very few), are usually referred to as 'inherited' from parents and grandparents. This neat philosophy of convenience can side step the issue and blame it onto others. It is true that one may observe a line of inheritance, but here as elsewhere that is only part of the story, for behind the visible there is an invisible world, hidden from the physical senses and the kind of thinking shackled to those senses. It is no less an observable fact that we, the sufferers of miasmatic diseases, brought them with us as a rag-bag of karma from previous lives.

It should be fairly obvious to everyone that venereal disease results from abuse of the sexual function. In the past evolution of humanity there has been much of this activity, particularly when division into the two sexes began. Over-stimulation of the sexual function resulted in loss of control, and these diseases were introduced to curb the activity.

The universal law of 'like attracts like' insists that the incarnating spirit fits perfectly into the family situation, hence the reflection of the same disease in the parents. The more diseased humanity is, the poorer the quality of spirit will it attract in its procreation.

Herein lies the implication for homœopathy: clean up the past karma of humanity by ridding it of miasmatic disease, and there will be fitting conditions for some of the more advanced spiritual beings to incarnate into the earthly life. This will in turn advance mankind's evolution towards a happier and more fulfilled existence. In this way is the homœopath the tool for evolution, let us make him a conscious and willing one.

> "To know the parents, observe the children, for
> by their fruits shall ye know them".

Miasmatic disease as observed by most homœopathic practitioners remains a physical and sometimes a mental/emotional phenomenon. But there is much that is hidden from the senses, and so the homœopath must use whatever other faculties he has developed along the way to understand his patient. The clairvoyant may more readily observe such things. Discharges, for instance, are not always just physical. For example, sometimes after an acute upheaval brought on by homœopathic treatment, it is as if a shadow has left the patient and the spirit has a greater hold on its vehicle, meaning that the subject appears much happier. Adjustments may also have been made to the lifestyle bringing the individual closer in line to their true purpose.

Karmic links are forged in the relationships that we have, and if those close to us should die we feel grief. Sometimes this feeling goes on too long and indeed may cripple the life. We may become manacled to the one who has passed on, who may also be linked to us and unable to progress further, being bound to the earth without a body. In such cases, remedies like NATRUM MUR, IGNATIA, SYPHILINUM and THYMUS GLAND are given for the picture of grief. These remedies and others can break the link of past attachment, freeing both incarnate and discarnate to continue with their evolutionary path.

Cleaning up the past can take a long time, often years, depending on the degree of ill health of the patient upon arrival. Freeing them is bringing them up to date, wiping the board clean. They will not then be subject to the same repetitive patterns of behaviour, but will find themselves more able to exercise choice and free will. They will be able to take more conscious control over their life, make their own decisions and take responsibility for the results. Those enclosed in the darkness of miasmatic disease are so crippled in their evolutionary position that they are unable to take any responsibility for themselves and usually lack any will to do so.

This is part of the great gift of homœopathy, to be able to bring someone up to date, to help them shift their karma. To help a being shine like the sun – what greater work is there? This sounds more like the real meaning of cure – spirit, mind and body in harmony.

It should be noted here that homœopathy is a tool that enables the patient to recognise, understand and overcome his difficulties, it does not do anything to the patient or provide anything that is not rightfully his. It rather gives him the chance to grasp the vision and make the most of the opportunity. The prescriber must learn to realise the needs of the patient, to recognise the path on which he is treading. In this way can mankind meet his true role as the instrument of nature, accelerating a process that would otherwise have taken much longer.

Certain remedies can be given for the specific purpose of wiping out karma, and it should be borne in mind by the practitioner that a patient may not progress until this is done. The chapters on the nosodes should be noted here. It is experienced that often a mere 'suspicion' that something is present within the patient is enough to justify the use of such a remedy. Equally it is unfortunate that such remedies are not fully known or appreciated, as so many cases have failed due to the lack of knowledge of the practitioner.

Karma is the link which runs through evolution, binding together many lives upon the thread of consciousness, from the past through to the present and into the future. But to appreciate it there must first be the awareness that there is an evolution. Many people think that they live but once and that death is the end. It is only in the last three hundred years or so that this thinking has been the norm, since mankind has attempted to describe the world in terms of his physical existence. Prior to this man was more aware that matter (form) was balanced by spirit; we are now told to 'prove' such a fact. Fortunately, the universe is so constructed that each must prove it to themselves by their own efforts. Behind the visible there is an invisible world, hidden from the crude senses of humanity, yet by the due development of the forces slumbering within us, it is possible to penetrate this hidden world.

At this time there is a rising tide of consciousness rediscovering the spiritual dimension to existence. This is one reason for the ascendence of homœopathy in recent years. It is the mass of humanity that will change medicine and society. Politicians, scientists, doctors and those who do not move with the tide will be left behind to form a further encrustation upon an already arthritic medical establishment, having to catch up later as best they may.

Aspiring homœopaths would do well to take courage and heed these words and not cringe before an intimidating authoritarian teaching, for the tides of evolution are with us, supporting and nurturing us when we stumble. What we need is dedicated physicians and we have to start with where we are and who we are now.

CHAPTER 2

DISEASE

Most of us have been educated from the start in the benefits of medical treatment as presented through our national health network. Along with this, doctors are revered for their learning and understanding. Somehow, we have become convinced that doctors know something that we do not, and that we need what they have. The advertisers know this one well, it is the psychology of dependence. For our part, we are all too willing to avoid taking responsibility for our own illnesses. This is a way of denying the truth about ourselves and the consequences of our own actions, preferring to dump it on another, who will 'tear us to pieces' for the privilege.

The Myth of Infection

The idea of 'infection' is a therapeutic philosophy of convenience, arising from a belief in a hostile environment and all the psychological disasters that are the consequence of such a basic attitude. Infection is a small piece of a large jigsaw puzzle. Yes, diseases are passed around, as is obvious to any school teacher when winter approaches, but disease needs a fertile soil in which to grow. We ourselves provide the environment for disease to develop.

Infection means very little; how can it? What understanding of illness does it provide? None. As a concept it terminates any further intelligent thought upon the subject. The truth and essence of disease is that it comes from within, always. After all, who is feeling ill? Who is doing the feeling?

Part of the understanding and benefit of homœopathic therapy is to take responsibility for our own condition. This does not imply passing judgement or blame. We do not need to extend or withdraw our approval. The essence of compassion is to love and heal at the same time as knowing that we are entirely responsible for our own condition. I do not use the word 'fault' here as it would imply blame and therefore rejection. Through our passage of evolution there is much wrong doing, both on a personal level and in larger group activity, but there are only lessons to be learned, and there is no 'fault' as such.

Our conventional medical misunderstanding is to extend sympathy when someone is ill because of the idea that people are victims through none of their own doing. This very idea creates victims. The orthodox system helps people as long as they appear helpless; this provides the opportunity for having a position of power and authority over the patient.

The true healer will love his patient while having compassion (not sympathy) for their weaknesses. She does not encourage their bad habits, or reinforce their helplessness, but gives them back a sense of their own power and responsibility.

Why do people look for a physician? The patient will seek assistance from a physician only when he is motivated to do so. Usually because his illness has reached a point of severity (pain) whereby it has sufficiently penetrated his consciousness to motivate him to action. Diagnosis occurs at the point where the patient meets the physician. From this it is apparent that the illness has a past (aetiology), is now in the present, and of course it must have some kind of future (prognosis).

All of this may sound pretty obvious, but the implication is this; that disease is a living process. Disease passes with us from the past, to the ever moving point of now, and into the future. Disease is therefore in a perpetual state of change and this change is dependent upon a number of things. The term 'diagnosis' however freezes the moment in time, serving to implant in us the idea that disease is static and subject only to the laws of matter. From this springs the conclusion that once a pathological change has taken place it is impossible to reverse the process. Such is the result of concrete thinking. Only the idea of aetiology and prognosis hint at any movement in disease, and then only in a limited way, and subject to preconceived ideas.

It is the nature of the concrete mind to divide and separate, when the truth is that all is one and one is all. The process of division and categorisation confuses the understanding of disease as a living process with one phase moving into another. All the various divisions of medical observation in reality phase one into another, and are all present at the same time.

Consider this within the context of homœopathic remedies. Most of our information regarding the remedies comes from systematically conducted provings according to the principles of Samuel Hahnemann. Information having been meticulously recorded on a daily basis as reported by those taking part in the proving. Other information comes from poisonings and clinical observation of the remedies in action. Homœopaths match these remedies to their patients on the basis of 'like cures like', and thereby produce their excellent results.

Thus having first observed disease as a continuous living process, homœopathic remedies are also considered as such. In the materia medicas the remedies are presented to us as remedy pictures, at first seeming like a list of disjointed symptoms, but with further study revealing a plan or pattern running through the symptomatology. By grasping this pattern or thread the whole may be realised by observing only a part. The patient will not suffer all the symptoms presented in the remedy picture at any one time. The homœopathic remedy is in fact a living process, the patient travelling from one aspect of it to another, revealing first this part and then the next.

Not only this, but also each remedy is linked to another, the one continuing where the other left off, producing a vast web of therapeutic interrelationships. One begins here to appreciate the idea that there are no diseases, only sick people. Herein lies also the fact that a patient requires a number of remedies on the road to health, as opposed to the idea that just one remedy will produce a cure; a misconception too often perpetrated in homœopathic education.

The remedies should be studied as living things, perpetually in motion and moving from one aspect of their nature to another. This brings the remedy pictures alive to the student, enabling the so-called essence of the remedy to be learned.

Equally so is it necessary to understand the essence of the patient. She will not be exactly the same as the remedy, but similar in some aspects, so that she requires it and that it will work to whatever degree it will. Human beings are very complex, having many facets to their spiritual, mental, emotional and physical selves. It is necessary to observe all these areas to be a successful practitioner.

A remedy may be successfully prescribed on mental symptoms alone if these are well marked. Or it may be more accurately and effectively prescribed by observing the essence of a person at that time. This kind of observation is preferable to listing symptoms projected by the patient via the prescriber onto paper. The way the patient is is similar to how you may know an old friend; with all their habits, strengths and weaknesses. In this way, any physical disease may be only briefly noted or seemingly ignored, yet, under the action of the remedy it will entirely disappear from the patient's being.

If this is so, and it is experienced by homœopaths every day, then how can disease by attributed solely to 'infection'? If mental, emotional and physical disease can all be treated under the same remedy action, then how can they be unrelated?

The disease belongs to the individual who has it. It is theirs by right. If a person manifests an infection then the one has attracted the other by the law of similars. Like attracts like – and like cures like – the law of homœopathy is a universal one.

The concept of infection has externalised the problem, as indeed man has done with his entire world. The weapons of war and the highly organised armies that wield them are an externalisation of our anger and aggression that we feel inside yet are unwilling to acknowledge. The abolition of weapons does not lie in CND but inside ourselves. What is it that makes us want to strike out at another when they step on our toe in a tube train? Until we have acknowledged and investigated that impulse the weapons will have to remain. We are competitive, divisive, and distrustful of one another when nature is trying to bring us together in 'cooperative bodies', an interesting phrase when considering the essence of disease.

We need a police force to suppress and deal with the ugly side of our externalised nature so that we may sit comfortably and not think about it. If we can use every day the doctrine of 'like cures like', then we must accept the universal law of 'like attracts like'; it is the same law differently expressed. This being so then we cannot separate the so called victim from the criminal; whatever the crime! We need burglars to remind us of the material wealth that we do not need. Burglars perform a valuable social service, and yet we choose to make them wrong, to punish and imprison them. What we should be doing is looking at our relationship with the material world. There is nothing wrong with material wealth, it is our relationship with it that is the problem.

The advent of terrorist activity is abhorrent for all to behold, yet has anyone in our political corridors really asked why they do it? The political response is always repressive, to behave in the same way, with force of arms and the threat of imprisonment. But the same activity done within society's respectable structure, with a uniform on, makes it alright. Since when has a disease been cured by suppression, by introducing a drug to force the body to conform? The disease will return at a later date or mutate into something more sinister. Disease is cured from within, gently and by encouraging the body to do its own job of healing. The lesson is there to be seen across society as a whole. The terrorist's activity, as a breakaway, self-interested unit is the essence of cancer; the disease projected individually by us into the society that we have all made and are so anxious to maintain.

We all have responsibility for ourselves and the consequences of our actions foremost, but also for the well-being of our fellows. This is the responsibility of service, of helping another on their way. It is when we surrender that responsibility to others, to doctors, politicians, the police, etc., that we pay the price. We try to ignore the process and its consequences until the pain and unhappiness become so bad that it forces us to take action on our own behalf.

The concept of 'infection' places the blame for disease firmly on an outside source, implying innocence on behalf of the infected. The psychological extension of this idea is to believe in an hostile environment, harbouring germs that are out to get us. Thus we need to insulate ourselves from other human beings in the belief that they too are the enemy.

The web of universal life is in truth supportive of its children, with all life forming as dew upon the web that maintains the integrity woven into it by its creator. In swaddling ourselves in weakness and ignorance we have leant on others who have been only too willing to manipulate for their own ends.

The Process of Cure

The idea of infection obliterates the real story of disease and its development through the ages. If we can for a moment look beyond it and accept that disease is a phenomenon which belongs to the individual who has it and to the human race alike, we may then begin to perceive it as a living, mutating Medusa. We must look in our own mirrors to have ourselves reflected back at us.

Disease is part of a living process within an individual who is in a perpetual state of flux according to the habits and flow of her life, and any medical treatment will create a change within this process. All change – whatever its nature – has an observable order of procedure. Curative or beneficial change of body, mind or soul proceeds from within, outwards. It also proceeds from above, downwards; and in organs from the major to the minor. A process in the opposite direction is an indication of deterioration and damage, although for those who lack understanding, it may in the short term appear to be otherwise. For example, it is rarely that a sufferer from chest, heart or spinal trouble will connect the present affliction with a past skin disease so nicely 'cured' with external applications, yet the connection is all too often there.

When peace and harmony has been created within, it will radiate outwards. This is the path to true health and it involves reconciling intention with action, wish with will, what you are with what you think you should be. The patient working from his side, with the homœopath working from his side. So the seeds of integrity are sown within, one day to blossom as a beautiful garden.

Ignorance, fear, vanity and a refusal to accept responsibility for ourselves drives us to apply cortizone creams to skin diseases, and take drugs of convenience to make discomfort go away; and usually one or two prescriptions of this nature will suffice, until the next time. However, the removal of an ugly eruption does not heal the process that produced it in the first place. The surgical excision of tumours, warts or moles will frustrate the quality of energy that produced them and drive them further inside that they may become more virulent and destructive in their activity. We prune roses in order that they should proliferate.

The process of suppression is detrimental to the life force. It is important that humanity recognise this now, for understood it will be sooner or later. The question here is how much suffering will be experienced on an ever increasing scale, before this fact impinges itself sufficiently upon the consciousness and action taken? Here pride and its shadow the philosophy of convenience are constant companions.

There is another way. The nature of homœopathic treatment is to reverse the process of degeneration, and to heal from the inside out. It is necessary that the patient fully appreciates this in order to work with the physician, and with his own forces and faculties along the path to better health. Homœopathy is centrifugal to the disease process, and it takes but a small shift in consciousness and habitual lines of thought for this to be appreciated.

The true treatment and cure of chronic disease takes time. This is one commodity few are willing to invest, even in themselves. A quick return for as little effort as possible is too often the nature of our society. The proper investment of time and persistence of effort will not be in vain, and will yield fruit for the future.

The drug treatment of disease is a process of disguise, seeming to make one thing appear like another, much like counterfeit money. We fool ourselves into thinking we are cured, while the habit of the lower mind for dividing and separating prevents us from recognising the connection between this disease and the last, and the next. In truth they are all one disease becoming ever more chronic as it is driven further into the being.

Antibiotics are a prime example of a therapeutic philosophy of convenience, suppressing and disguising the disease process throughout the being. In using antibiotics we manage to avoid taking responsibility for the disease process at that time. Their repeated use severely damages the immune system, contributing considerably to the breakdown of this faculty in recent years. Also their repeated use in local septic conditions helps to create a constitutional sepsis, and its natural result – cancer. This is clearly observable by taking many medical histories over a period of time.

We have taken a very long time to produce our diseases in their present form, so we must invest some time in being rid of them. Under truly curative treatment disease will not disappear overnight, and the path to health may be strewn with potholes.

It is often said of homœopathic treatment that the patient gets worse before improving. Herein lies the key to change and its relationship with disease. Almost all of us will have had disease suppressed by drug treatment, external applications and vaccination at some time in our lives. Together with disease inherited from previous generations, this constitutes the principle encrustation of ill health. Add to this the bad emotional attitudes that we have, and the poor daily habits in which we indulge, such as smoking, drinking and bad diet, and this all fuels the situation. The homœopathic remedies will release these things, not all at once, but gradually and over a period of time. The last things to appear will be the first to go, and the first things to arrive will be the last to leave. In this way not only the symptoms, but the cause of illness is healed, leaving in its place a greater presence of health and well-being.

As change takes place, so the inconvenience of its passage may be felt, and sometimes an exaggeration or aggravation of symptoms will be experienced. This will soon pass, to be replaced by relief and a change in the original symptom complex with the patient feeling improvement within themselves. This last observation is an important factor, it pertains to the integrity of the inner being; the patient may know that they are better, when the physician may not.

A point of change or aggravation is also known as the healing crisis, and the patient while immersed within it may consider themselves worse rather than better. It is important here to take the long-term point of view, and to hold in mind that the process is one of change, where the patient may already be improving in themselves and yet identify themselves with the upheavals of their physical body.

An eruption on the skin is often produced after taking homœopathic remedies. This may even be one recognised by the patient as having been 'cured' by external applications some years earlier. The return of an old condition is a good sign of disease travelling from the inside to the outside. The skin is, after all, an organ of elimination and it is principally our vanity that drives in what is attempting to come out. A cold or other acute catarrhal condition is another frequently observed condition that arises as the body goes about its own work in ridding itself of poison and toxicity.

The physical body has an intelligence of its own. It will gather toxic material and push it out at some point of convenience, creating a local sepsis; so often mistaken as an 'infection' and driven back in again. When pushed back in it will lead to such phenomena as acute otitis media, tonsilitis, abscess, boils and mastoid affections – this last being very profound in its ramifications. Other undesirable matter is pushed to the extremities where it is least likely to cause any serious damage, hence the common occurence of 'arthritis' in the hands and feet.

The homœopath must be on his guard not to become embroiled in the drama of acute aggravations under homœopathic remedies, for they are all to the good, and when the storm is over a real threshold in the healing processs will have been passed. Only in extreme circumstances, such as great pain or danger to life is it necessary to intervene. Generally, if the vitality is good then the life is not in danger, only if it is feeble is there cause for concern. However, low potency remedies, biochemic tissue salts and Bach Flower Remedies may be safely used to lighten the load of a homœopathic aggravation. When using low potencies in such an instance it is important not to use antidotes or antagonistic remedies to the main remedy.

Sometimes quite severe upheavals can be experienced, though these are usually rare. Even so, it is important for both patient and physician to ride the storm and await the sweeter air. The healing process is often not a smooth one, such is the position that we have placed ourselves in with relation to disease and its suppression. A certain amount of inconvenience must often take place if the healing is to be thorough and true. It is important for the patient to realise this, so that he does not at some point give up, thinking himself to be worse, or that the inconvenience is not worth it. The cultivation of a long-term point of view, so alien to our culture, is worthwhile.

It is equally important for the homœopath to witness the healing process, then his courage will be backed by some experience. The way to defeat fear is with knowledge, and knowledge is not earned by the faint-hearted. Homœopathy is a young science worthy of development and all its practitioners are pioneers. It is they who are breaking new ground in the field of human experience and are the first to make mistakes and be criticised by those who sit behind them in comfort, waiting to walk down a path made easy for them by those who have gone before.

Emotional aggravations may also be experienced, for example, acute depression, fear or irritability, but the emotional abscess will also burst and with it will pass a shadow from the patient leaving in its wake a well-being hitherto unrecognised. As the picture unfolds, the pattern of disease changes and with it the personality. The more negative aspects become transformed to more positive ones of right activity and goodwill to one's fellows. This is the great gift of homœopathy, the transformation of personality.

What is Health?

Most of us consider that if we are not ill then we must therefore be healthy, or that if we are fit we must also enjoy health. What in this case is meant by 'ill', and by 'health'? When we ride the trains and buses of our cities, observe the countenance of those who sit around us; do we see health? If we are ourselves in the same state, we are bound to see little difference between our own health and that of those we observe. Thus many make the assumption that all are healthy unless they have been diagnosed as ill by the doctors.

In western society disease is defined in terms of pathology or morbid physiology of the physical body only. No recognition is provided for disease existing in other vehicles of expression, ie. the vital body, emotions, mind or spirit. Yet many observers, including psychologists, rightly conclude that many diseases begin in the powerful mental or emotional realm.

If this is so, then there must be a moment when morbid physiology and pathology is confined within these less dense vehicles before it reaches the physical vehicle where it may be recognised as physical disease. Only when disease has reached the physical are most of us prepared to acknowledge that we have a diseased state. Prior to this we may feel unwell but as the doctors can find no morbid change in the physical vehicle we are pronounced not ill or healthy.

It is the patient who really knows that he is unwell, not the doctor. We have placed ourselves in a dangerous situation here because we are taught that if the doctors can find nothing wrong, then there is nothing wrong, and our malaise is 'all in the mind'. Because of this we fail to acknowledge to ourselves that we are in a state of disease, and attempt to continue life as normally as possible.

If absence of disease does not constitute health then what does? It is not fitness, though this may give a semblance of it. Some of the fittest people we may also observe as being the most diseased, both physically and emotionally. Health is a radiant state of being in which all the vehicles of expression are united in the service of the spirit. The healthy person is able to rejoice in just being in the present moment, without recourse to dwelling in the past or the future.

This is not just a piece of wishful fancy, but is a demonstrable reality, achieved by very few but achievable by many more. One must first acknowledge the deficit. The road to good health is a bumpy one, there are pitfalls and potholes, times when things may seem to be worse rather than better. Persistance and the willingness to change, to take a step in the dark, are required; thus does the butterfly emerge from the chrysallis. Homœopathy is just a tool in this process, yet it remains the best one that I know.

Whilst most people have felt ill at some time in the past, and therefore know what it is, very few have felt radiant health, and so it remains an idea outside the knowledge gained by experience. We consider our regular state of being as that of health without realising that any further gain may be achieved. This is a perilous complacency when considering the apalling decline in the general health of the population.

When enough people suffer from a particular complaint at some time in their life, or as a result of a particular life process, it is considered to be normal. It is considered normal that mothers suffer depression after childbirth. It is considered normal that people suffer from joint troubles or rheumatism after middle age. Normal for the menopause to be accompanied by hot flushes, excessive periods, depression and other emotional disorders. Normal that people produce warts and moles. Normal to suffer with catarrh. Normal for menstrual periods to be painful or preceded by emotional upheaval. It is the norm to fear disease and have our children vaccinated less they 'catch' some dreadful illness.

It is normal for us to go to the doctor and have all these conditions suppressed by drugs repeatedly, without further thought, and with no connection made in the mind that this illness may be the result of the suppression of the last. This is the case with breast cancer. Most breast cancers appear after the menopause, it should therefore be worth considering that breast cancers are not primarily of the breast, but rather we should look at the primary generative organs. The cause may usually be found in a study of the menstrual history, disorders that are found to coexist with the menstrual history, and the bad management of the same. These things are blindly stumbled over or passed coldly by as so much menstrual disorder is considered to be normal.

It is becoming normal for people to die of cancer. This is not the natural inheritance of humanity, but the weakness in which it has modelled itself.

It takes but a small shift of consciousness to realise the devastating consequences that drugs can have on us. A drug will compel the body to do something. By contrast, the homœopathic remedy will encourage the body to do its own work. It is often claimed by pharmaceutical manufacturers that drugs are safe or less harmful if prescribed skillfully by doctors; but if there is less danger how can there be no danger? There is always a price to be paid for taking any drug, however small it may be, and however expedient the reason. Drugs have done much to suppress acute disease, and in so doing have increased the level of chronic disease with all its sinister consequences.

Chapter 2

Acute Disease

The onset of acute disease is fast and the pace is rapid. The degree of pain and inflammation may be high, often accompanied by a general increase in temperature and the formation of pus. Its impact may be sufficiently alarming to leave those in attendance with a feeling of helplessness. Psychologically the feeling of 'must do something' often motivates us into the wrong kind of action, and unless we really know what to do for the best, action may make the patient worse rather than better.

Knowing what to do for an acute disease implies prior knowledge, gained as ever through the field of experience. Since most people do not possess sufficient experience, recourse to drugs is often taken; a harsh action that may mean the patient will not die, but will not on the other hand really get better. It is the fear of death which is ever present in these situations. And for the physician, it is also the belief that if the patient does die, they can satisfy their conscience that they did 'all that was possible'.

If there is great pain, or if the patient's life is in imminent danger, then action must be taken immediately. The art here is in knowing what action to take based on a true knowledge of what is going on. The situation must be assimilated by the attending physician in the space of a few moments. What is therefore required, above anything else, is a quiet and detached presence, despite the surrounding clamour of those in a more chaotic state of being. Part of the art of medical practice is masterly inactivity, during which time the physician may observe his patient.

> "If you can keep your head
> When all about you are losing their's
> and blaming it on you"

Kipling's lines are the best prescription for the attending physician. The other necessary requirements for successfully dealing with an acute situation are a thorough knowledge of the Materia Medica and an understanding of the disease process.

Disease falls into two basic categories: acute and chronic.

Chronic disease lives with the person in the physical body. It is often in a relatively inactive state, and can go virtually unnoticed, except by those who know how to look for it. However, from time to time the organism will stage a violent and often spectacular attempt to rid itself of its chronic malady. In this situation the body may be temporarily removed from normal daily functions due to the great upsurge of acute disease symptoms. Thus we can see that acute as well as chronic disease comes from within.

After the storm has passed, the chronic condition may return, which was not observable during the acute phase. In many cases the chronic symptoms will have improved in some way, revealing that the body has been successful at throwing off some of its disease content. This being so points to acute disease being a positive occurence, and therefore best left for the body to deal with in its own intelligent way. This point has great importance when considering the acute diseases of childhood.

However, if during the acute phase some drug therapy has been administered, then the acute will be suppressed and driven back into the organism. This will reduce the vitality and weaken the immune system. If further suppressions of the acute phases take place, then the patient will grow deeper into his chronic state with the underlying disease becoming more serious and sinister in its consequences. This is what we have done with our drug therapies. Acute explosions of disease have been misunderstood as unacceptable and have had the lid pushed on them, leading to our chronic diseases revealing themselves so devastatingly in later years. Similarly have we filled up our prisons and mental institutions so that we need to build more and more new facilities and produce yet more poor wretches to continue filling them up.

The psychology of acute disease is underpinned by the spirit of 'must do something', this is the basis of our national health system. It can be observed how the sense of panic and fear spreads from the afflicted to those in attendance, who will then demand that something must be done, meanwhile scripting in their minds their innocence in the drama and being ready to blame it on another if anything goes wrong.

People do not like to feel helpless. To be able to exercise detachment and observe a distressing situation knowing that it is best to do nothing at the present moment takes some doing, but is well worthy of achievement. This does not mean that one needs to indulge in passivity on other levels, to project healing and love to the sufferer by using the mind to direct the power of the emotions may do more good than any physical action taken.

CHAPTER 3

THE VITAL FORCE

Samuel Hahnemann spoke of the 'vital force' and how it exerted power and influence over the physical body. This can be observed during homœopathic practice when the patient feels improved in themselves, their energy increases, and then their physical disease is cured after taking the correct remedy. The homœopathic remedy appears to act directly on this vital force, which ultimately brings about changes in the physical body.

At death the vital force leaves the physical body, leaving it a lifeless shell. In life the vital force motivates the physical body, and is what we may see on the faces of our companions as the joy of life. The vital force contains all aspects of human expression. It is the manifestation of life energy, and without it the physical vehicle has no animation or sensation. It is the vehicle of disease and disorder, expressing them through the physical body by means of morbid disease symptoms. It is said that disease is registered first in the vital force, and may be observed there by an acute observer.

The vital force may be considered as a layer of energy, a vehicle of human expression, not solid like the physical body, but having some substance. It is almost identical in shape to the physical body, but larger, extending a few inches beyond the physical. The vital force is perhaps even more complex in its nature and function than the physical body. Being an energy force it has a magnetic field, rather like that of the earth.

The vital body, like all the others other than the physical, and including the spiritual, has long been denied in our society. They have remained the knowledge of mystics, clairvoyants and occultists and the subject of scorn by scientists.

It is the energy vehicle, or the vital force, that motivates the physical body, and contains within it the impression of habits past and present, together with some aspects of memory. It is these inappropriate and outworn habits that lead to so much disease in the physical body. They form patterns of behaviour no longer required by evolution. The inertia of the being, or the unwillingness to relinquish these habits, under an ever-increasing pressure to do so, creates disease, decay and corruption within. To be well, to be cured in the full sense of the word, involves change from old habits to new; the kind of change that can be experienced under homœopathic therapy.

The old habitual lines of behaviour continually indulged in, reveal an increasing inability to adapt to the environment, itself an ever evolving process. The idea is often put forward that disease is the inability to adapt to the environment. An unwillingness to fulfil the will of one's own spirit is another way of expressing the same thing.

Also contained within the vital or etheric vehicle is the phantom image of past disease. That is, diseases inherited or not properly dealt with by the being, or trapped by the use of suppressive drug treatments. This constitutes part of the karmic disease of the past, and if the person is to be fully cured, must be removed during therapy – often by the use of the disease nosodes. It is by observing this shadow in the vital body that we may suspect something to be wrong before physical symptoms appear. The taking of a proper case history is most helpful.

It is also necessary to understand the vital body as the vehicle that builds, maintains and repairs the physical body. Here lie implications as to how homœopathy works.

During our daily lives considerable damage is wrought on the physical body by the detrimental effects of negative mental and emotional activity, together with wrong nutrition, the taking of drugs and stimulants and physical trauma. The physical body requires sufficient sleep and rest. It is during sleep that the higher vehicles depart, leaving the vital body to repair the physical. In the morning on waking, the experience should be one of refreshment as the person re-enters the physical body. If this is not so, the vitality itself is lacking in some way, or tissues are being worn out faster than they can be repaired or there is toxicity shifting around the body.

During disease the vital body is affected in a similar way to the physical. The administration of the homœopathic remedy stimulates the vital force to perform its work, on itself and on its physical counterpart. Thus, during homœopathic remedy aggravations nothing is introduced that was not already there; the discomfort results from the shifting around of certain component parts and the elimination of toxicity from the physical and vital bodies.

Here is revealed the true nature of the potentised homœopathic remedy – it is itself vital not physical. The trituration and succussion of substances breaks down their molecular and atomic structure, releasing energy. When diluted no traceable matter is left. The remedy is now vital or etheric, and by its very nature acts directly on the vital body. The energy of the remedy when correctly prescribed is unleashed on the vital force and this is transmitted to its physical vehicle, which behaves like putty under its influence. Thus do we observe the amazing results from dynamic homœopathic remedies, the asthma that disappears overnight, the necrosed bone of an arthritic hip that regenerates, the cancer that decreases and disappears; because the volume of what produced them in the first place is turned down.

In looking at the vital force and its nature, we begin to understand just a little of disease, its hidden ways and physical expression. Because we cannot observe something with our physical senses does not mean it does not exist. Many times this has been said and heard but not really understood.

The vital force is best understood as a battery which during life may become flat but responds well to recharging. However, towards the end of its life this battery becomes weaker, and recharging is no longer the dynamic input that it once was. At death the vital vehicle departs to disintegrate in much the same way as the physical. It is interesting to note that occultists consider the vital body to be part of the physical vehicle, and therefore itself 'physical'. The vital force is the subject matter of Kirlian photography, which photographs electromagnetic energy. It is also readily observed by psychics and clairvoyants, together with the astral vehicle (emotional body). The action of the homœopathic remedy on the vital body involves the same processes as nuclear physics, but nuclear physics is usually only considered as that which occurs outside ourselves and thus much more interesting to observe.

The vital body may suffer damage much like the physical. It is weakened by chronic disease and by drug suppression which it holds like a shadow in its structure. Its efficiency therefore can be somewhat curtailed, and its ability to repair the physical body stunted. The answer to many immune deficiency diseases can be found here, as it is the vital body and its link with the physical, via the nervous system, that determines the health of the immune system.

It is through direct contact with the nervous system that the vital body acts on the physical. The dynamic substance of the homœopathic remedy is absorbed into the nervous system, usually sub-lingually. Purely material substances, such as pharmaceutical drugs, will be absorbed into the physical body usually via the blood stream. The energy quantum of the homœopathic remedy must identify with the next stage up from the physical, that of vitality, using the link of the nervous system. The energy of the homœopathic remedy is made available for the vital body via the nervous system, and by return the vital force acts upon the physical body, using the nervous system as a means of transmission.

The gateway for this transmission of energy between the physical nervous system and the vital force is the spleen. This process can be observed by clairvoyants when the energy of the sun is absorbed by the spleen, converted into life force by the vital body, and distributed throughout the branches of the nervous system, flowing like a rose-coloured fluid through the whole system to the nerve endings. If the physical spleen has been surgically removed, the etheric double remains and has to do the job.

CHAPTER 4

CHILDHOOD ILLNESSES AND IMMUNISATION

The acute diseases of childhood are the brief flowering of the seeds of miasmatic disease that punctuate the human race at every new generation. Once again we content ourselves with the illusion that they are 'caught' via bacteria and viruses from a hostile environment, and no further consideration is given to the matter. Except in so far as they may be handed round by children of like constitutions, they are no such thing. Not all children will produce all the diseases, but most children will produce one or more at different times.

An outbreak of a childhood illness occurs as one child awakens it in another. It is not that something is passed on to another that the other did not previously have, and is therefore an innocent victim. The bacteria associated with the disease may be observed once the sickness has taken hold, but it is likely that it was there also during health. The inner environment of the physical vehicle has been changed so that the bacteria can proliferate. Like any life form, bacteria will struggle for its own survival, thus stimulating inflammation, fever, etc. in order to make its contribution to an environment compatible with its existence.

The childhood illnesses are ancient diseases lying dormant in the human script, and the incarnation of a fresh vitality brings with it the opportunity to cast off an old burden. Thus our children produce mumps, measles, whooping cough, etc. according to their individual expression. In our ignorance we mostly remain unaware of how important these irritating little diseases are, and proceed to suppress them with immunisations and drugs. We similarly choose to remain mostly ignorant of how dangerous in the longer term such suppression is.

Imagine how wonderful it is for a new life with much vitality to be able to cast off old shadows. If you observe closely enough you will see how a child improves in health, well-being and development after a childhood disease has come and gone, depending of course on how much more miasmatic effluent remains to come out in other forms. This improvement in health is particularly visible after measles, which is probably the deepest of the childhood illnesses.

The childhood illnesses are the visible manifestations of the miasms of Hahnemann. They represent the level of disease that lies deepest in the past. Largely, they are not diseases of this lifetime, but of previous incarnations and family karma. The child in his early years has the opportunity to throw off these miasms in the form of childhood diseases, so that much of that old disease of the past is not carried forward into his life, crippling his constitution and subsequently being passed on to the next generation. However, because this process is not understood, the elimination process is frequently suppressed. We are simply not permitted to be ill.

Not only are the symptoms of the illness suppressed, but even more seriously, immunisation is used to viciously suppress any likely manifestation. Firstly, this does not work because the children may still experience the diseases, but usually in a modified form so that a proper diagnosis is missed. Secondly, a mutation of far more terrible consequences may occur, creating more serious diseases including meningitis, arthritis and cancer later in life.

If a proper manifestation is allowed, the childhood diseases are harmless and thoroughly beneficial. Any serious consequences experienced are not directly a result of the disease itself, but indicate that the child is ill at the constitutional level. Children are not all born to the same level of health, they show their individuality in this respect as in any other. If the general constitution of the child is poor or diseased then the acute diseases of childhood will be more serious or intensely experienced. Immunisation will render the constitution even poorer. This is one reason why the incidence of chronic diseases is increasing so greatly.

How do childhood illnesses represent specific miasms? Mumps generally corresponds to the sycotic miasm, or that disease process that comes from gonorrhoea when passed on through the generations. Mumps has a metastasis, either visibly or invisibly, to the testes in boys and ovaries in girls. If suppressed by immunisation then a pervertion of the sexual function is likely to occur, especially in boys, with frightening consequences for the future.

Chicken pox and its partner disease, shingles, is a manifestation of the syphilitic miasm. Interestingly, children often produce this disease after being given the homœopathic remedy TUBERCULINUM; or they may produce it as an indication of needing the remedy. This betrays the syphilitic aspect of Tuberculosis, which is otherwise a largely sycotic disease.

Measles is the disease of the psoric miasm, the miasm of underfunction, infestation and belief in failure. Measles is probably the deepest of all the childhood diseases, and children are often observed to grow and flourish after having it. It is particularly dangerous to suppress this disease.

Whooping cough is a tubercular manifestation. After the immunisation for pertussis the children may still produce it in the form of an unrelenting cough with much mucous and sometimes vomiting, but without the whoop. This cough may continue for months, and will coincide with, as in other suppressions, a general lowering in the vitality. The sparkle will disappear from the child's eyes and she will look vacant and unhappy. This condition is not recognised as disease and is, sadly, today considered as normal.

The Case Against Immunisation

In the past few years there has emerged a growing concern among many at our passive acceptance of the need to immunise our children, and the terrible fear and guilt perpetrated at any sign of dissent.

The propaganda machine of government and medical authorities alike has proved ruthlessly efficient in the case of immunisation, at persuading us to accept an authoritarian dogma that banquets on our ignorance. It seems that in matters of health especially, we have been willing to surrender responsibility for ourselves to others, who are themselves living in darkness. How deep is our ignorance and complete our slumber in allowing us to stand by while foreign proteins, live viruses and septic matter is injected into the bloodstream of our children?

With daily reports to the contrary quickly dismissed by self-interested authorities, how can we honestly claim that there is proof beyond reasonable doubt that artificial immunisation is a safe and effective protection against so-called 'infectious' disease and is in no way injurious to health, and that the threat of the corresponding diseases is sufficiently great to justify mass inoculation of the people? Not only has no such proof ever been given, but also how can we possibly justify the mass employment of vaccines against diseases such as measles and mumps that are not only harmless but are positively beneficial for our children to experience?

It is a fact that much disease was on the decline towards the end of the last century, before vaccines became fashionable. Despite the claims of medical authorities to have eradicated disease by inoculation, it is proper sewerage and waste disposal, improvements in public health and general sanitation that have marked the decline of infectious diseases in the last hundred years. The great cholera epidemics of the 1850s and before were not halted in London until a proper sewerage system was built. As living standards have continued to increase so the diseases have declined, punctuated briefly by a return when standards have dropped.

Tuberculosis for instance is a disease of fear, depletion and poverty, and is seen to return in western societies when these conditions prevail. Its suppression by drugs and vaccines assured its mutation into cancer, and the ear, nose and throat troubles experienced today by so many of our children.

The evolution of vaccination has rested upon a fatal and fundamental error in the understanding of the nature of disease – that disease is haphazardly caught by the innocent through the transfer of microbes from the atmosphere. Also that these microbes constitute the whole of the disease, and that they may be eradicated by inoculation, thus removing the disease from mankind in its entirety.

The truth is that disease comes from within, always, from its beginnings, and through its manifestations and decline. It may be passed from one to another only by affinity, in much the same way as a magnet passes its power to a steel pin in close proximity. The pin is magnetised by virtue of what it is and not as a 'fault' of the magnet. Similarly a disease may be 'transmitted' to one in close proximity to the diseased because of what they are; their standard of health physically, morally, mentally, emotionally and spiritually. The disease is already inside them, the external manifestation alone is triggered by the presence of another with the disease. Had the pin been made of wood, it would not have become magnetised.

When sufficient of a population share the same level of poor health and living conditions, then there is an epidemic, but some will have it and others will not. This does not deny the existence of microbial organisms being passed from one to another, but merely places this concept in its proper place amidst the greater vista of degenerative processes. In other words, it takes a fertile soil for a seed to grow.

In my extensive homœopathic practice, and that of others, there is and has always been a continuous flow of observable evidence illustrating the appalling damage wrought by vaccines upon our children. A morbid pathology is set up for a lifetime.

We have no long-term point of view. We delude ourselves into thinking that if our children do not suffer acute disease then they are healthy. Fear takes over, persuading us that if they do get an illness then surely it will be fatal and therefore be our fault. There are and always have been those who will exploit fear in others. If we look back on history we may scoff at those who displayed real fear over a religious or social concern in a given age, and quietly laugh to ourselves as we see the greater overview of encircling events, revealing a deluded people. The problem is we smugly consider ourselves to be above these things and this is what blinds us. The truth is, the scientist has superseded the religionist. The doctor has taken over from the priest. The blind faith of the congregation, however, has not changed. Threats of death and disease have displaced hell-fire and eternal damnation. If we could only overcome our fear we would realise there isn't a scrap of truth in either.

The best defence against disease is health. I imagine there can be little controversy over this statement. Health, however, is never standardised, it is individual and is at different levels, good or bad, within all of us. A certain level of health is there from birth, where it is added to or subtracted from according to our activities and what we put into our bodies. If, as we have said, health and disease come from within how then can the injection of proteins, viruses and septic material into the bloodstream increase the level of health?

The apparent disappearance of diseases after inoculation is a deception, a morbid concealment of the truth; a savage illusion for which we pay a terrible price. The fact is, after immunisation the diseases mutate, they change, go underground, only to emerge years later as some 'new' disease or as evidence of an increase of chronic disintegration such as cancer.

Smallpox is not cured or eradicated at all, it just will not be seen in that form anymore. Some researchers have made a convincing link between the suppression of smallpox and the subsequent emergence of AIDS. Certainly in the last one hundred years sufficient of the race have been vaccinated to ensure that everyone has a version of smallpox passed down through the generations, and emerging as various mutations.

In effect we are trading measles and mumps for such diseases as asthma, rheumatoid arthritis, cancer and leukaemia. There is little doubt that many chronic diseases are on the increase, afflicting younger and younger people. Yet the connection with inoculation is barely questioned.

What may not be so obvious and yet is even more sinister is the relationship between immunisation as an agent of suppression, and crime and mental illness. The connection between certain drugs used to control disease, and undesirable behaviour is known, but that vaccines are also responsible in this area is not. The hyperactive, wild and uncontrollable behaviour of children, both individually and in groups, is often the direct effect of vaccines.

The situation regarding vaccination is becoming ever more urgent. A whole industry has been set up around it with balance sheets and tax returns involved. Individuals make their reputations by it and pay their mortgages with it. It is for these reasons that resistance to its abolition will be severe. Fear, self-preservation and self-interest will rule the day, but sadly these arguments will not make the effect upon the human race any less devastating. The striving for more and more vaccines parallels the steady decline in our health, and one day, either through greater consciousness or the gathering storm clouds of disaster, inoculation will be abandoned. Let us hope that consciousness will prevail, for how much more terrible disease and suffering will have to be endured before this point is reached?

It is the people who must decide what they want. As they change and move on so will the scientist, doctor and legislators be forced to move on after. A people who will not take charge of their own lives and be responsible for themselves and their families will become subject to control by the government of the day. Within the last thirty years a growing consciousness has emerged, mostly as a result of transmission of what was once the exclusive property of the East. With it has come a greater awareness of disease and its psychological origin, and in its wake a realisation that mankind is not a piece of mobile protoplasm, but is indeed a spiritual integrity.

It is hailed by the medical establishment, media and government policy alike that immunisation is a safe form of protection against disease, holding little or no risk. There are, however, many spectacular disasters following vaccination featuring neurological and brain damage, and death. It is also stated by the orthodox medical authority that if a child is suffering from a chronic ailment such as asthma then they should not be immunised, as the risk of immunisation damage is greater to a child with such diseases. There is then acknowledged to be some risk after all.

To those who observe human behaviour very closely the evidence of immunisation damage in every child who has been immunised becomes increasingly more obvious, and the observer ever more sensitive to it. The tragedy is to see people damaging their children while under the illusion that they are doing good. The difficulty here is how to appeal to people without stirring the fear generated by the orthodox medical profession. A child is these days first immunised at around two months old. The problem here is how to assess the damage done by immunisation at this early age, as we cannot measure the full capacity of the being beforehand as against her performance afterwards. What a risk, and so blindly followed!

There are those who have not been immunised at all, and if you take the time to observe you will find they are very different from the rest of us. The spark of life, the light of the spirit, is dimmed in a child who has been immunised. In the child that has not been immunised and is otherwise reasonably healthy, you can observe the sheer joy and love of life. It is a quality of being, an untainted expression of life itself which may be observed.

The primary and most common physical consequence of immunisation in a child is an increase in catarrh. This follows particularly quickly after the DPT inoculation. Probably the greatest tragedy of all is that we consider this catarrh to be normal in children. After all, every child appears to have it to some degree. And of course almost every child is immunised – so who can tell the difference? Not only are we prepared to damage our children with these products being injected directly into the bloodstream, but the resulting damage we accept as normal. We are learning to accept sub-standard humanity as normal.

The catarrh suffered by the child after inoculation is of the chronic kind. The parents usually say "he has a cold all the time", or "she keeps catching colds". Sometimes the nose runs with thick catarrh all the time, the head is stuffy and she cannot breathe properly, especially at night. Then there are the ear troubles that afflict some, the acute otitis media, a painful catarrhal congestion of the middle ear, often with a gathering of pus which may burst the ear drum thus creating a discharge. This is always greeted with some alarm and a considerable amount of fear, the result being a dose of antibiotics. Then the child really is on the downward spiral. The process usually keeps repeating itself. Frequent tonsilitis is also common, again greeted with a hefty dose of antibiotics – driving the illness towards the kidneys and all the unpleasant consequences of inflammations in that area.

Since physiologically speaking the amount of pus and catarrh in the body is a measure of disease, it does not appear that vaccination plus antibiotics have made our children any healthier. Listlessness, boredom, depression, antisocial and sometimes violent behaviour, a lack of interest in life and a general lack of energy are the observable psychological results.

Vaccination increases the level of pus and catarrh in the body. The presence of these reduces a person's ability to be effective in a practical sense. They become disconnected from their purpose or activity in much the same way as a camera lens becomes dirty or out of focus, giving a distorted image – in other words, something other than what is true. The greater the level of toxicity in the body the less grip the spirit has over its physical vehicle. Children with a high level of catarrh will appear vacant or even sit and stare for long periods, remaining inactive. Such children are treated as being stupid when all they are is ill and if given the right medical attention will flourish. Clearing out some of the damaging effects of immunisation is one of the great benefits of homœopathy.

CHAPTER 5

THE HEART AND CIRCULATION

The heart and circulation are an expression of the fluid balance within the body and are concerned with the ebb and flow of such. Here expressed is the heart's connection (physiologically) with the kidneys. When either of these organs are diseased an imbalance of bodily fluids results, each putting a strain upon the other. The balance of fluids in the body forms a physiological counterpart to the emotional realm, the health or otherwise of the emotional life being reflected in the fluid balance within the individual, thus profoundly affecting the function of both heart and kidneys.

Powerful emotions such as grief or shock will create an imbalance in the bodily fluids. There may be a dryness in one area and an over-abundance in another, such as, a dryness of the skin and mucus membranes with an attendant thirst which is not satisfied; or a dryness in one area of the body with oedema experienced in another. A patient may become convinced he drinks more than he passes through his kidneys and bladder. An inability to express emotions freely can produce such an imbalance, which on the surface may seem harmless enough. After all, the person may not feel ill or consider anything to be wrong, however, the story is written upon the countenance and whilst not presenting a problem at present, the prognosis may be predictable. The judicial employment of homœopathic treatment can not only correct the immediate imbalance but can teach and direct the patient, even if somewhat unconsciously at first, to realise more fully the powers within him; who he is and how to meet his own needs.

We may here refer to the homœopathic remedy NATRUM MUR, the great water balancer. It has within its picture dryness, thirst, oedema and – emotionally – the trauma of shock, distress and disappointment. The anatomy of a remedy can be studied in various layers of pathology; from emotional to functional to actual tissue change and degeneration in heart and kidney disease. These form the pathological keynotes of the remedy.

The homœopathic practitioner is ideally placed, as observer, to detect heart disease in the making, before it becomes physical pathology. Once the symptoms have become life-threatening for the patient he may be too fearful to seek proper treatment, and run into the arms of the conventionalists with their drugs.

Melancholy, sadness and anxiety tend to be the emotional keynotes of heart disease, with an attendant anti-social attitude, nostalgia and sentimentality. A closed attitude, an unwillingness to communicate or to forgive, weigh heavily on the heart's qualities of expression and in time may lead to functional disorder and eventual pathology. Exhaustion and sudden collapse is usually a sign of heart distress when life is lived at such a pace that the heart gets worn out. Hard work and grief play their part in wearing down a good heart.

Pain down the left arm to the fingers, with numbness and tingling, is a classic symptom of heart disease, but the same may occur in the right arm, as effected in some homœopathic remedy pictures such as NATRUM MUR and LILIUM TIGRINUM. The inability to place the left arm behind the back, or to raise the arms above the head are also tell-tale signs.

Most heart disease is syphilitic in origin, especially that affecting the valves and the aorta. Aortic aneurism is a well known syphilitic affection.

The condition of the heart reflects much upon the level of toxicity in the body. Patients with heart conditions treated homœopathically often respond by producing colds, flus, and acute catarrhal conditions. These are a good sign and should not be prevented or suppressed, for in this way is the patient's heart and circulation improved and the individual's health greatly enhanced.

Most homœopathic remedies used in the treatment of heart disease are powerful poisons, which, if well studied will be seen to produce a considerable degree of sepsis within the human economy. The snake poisons for instance act by decomposing the blood.

Much heart disease is blamed on the destructive indulgent

habits of our age, namely overuse of alcohol, smoking, eating poor food, and the repeated use of drugs either pleasure-orientated or doctor-prescribed. Whilst all this is demonstrably true, there do exist other emotional and perhaps more subtle causes of disease in this area. The heart is the centre of much emotional power and the general level of human development is at present centred in this area. Mankind lives in his heart and not in his head – the mind is the area he is striving to develop.

In ancient expression, the sun rules the heart and its qualities. One who expresses this flow of energy properly through their personality shines or radiates their individuality and expression of God. To 'shine like the sun' is no easy task and usually involves the process of rebirth, we being the child. It means being open, willing to communicate, and with no secrets. We have nothing to be ashamed of and nothing to hide.

Africa is a continent ruled by the sun, whose people are learning to express positively the qualities of the heart centre. They are a 'sunny' and open people who traditionally spend much time singing and laughing, and derive much pleasure from music, movement and dance. They have also embraced the Christian religion, with its tendency for sentimentality, richly expressed in their group activity.

This is all in marked contrast to northern European nations, many of whom are comparatively subdued, always controlled and express little. Withdrawal and secrecy are the suppression or negative aspects of the heart centre. The emotions are held in, to be released only when the build-up creates an explosion and emotional flood-tide, or privately and in controlled circumstances. The release of this suppression is the weeping at sentimental films or highly charged music.

Weeping is connected to bleeding, which is why many women are tearful before the menstrual period, as the pressure or build-up of energy finds an outlet prior to the loss of menstrual blood. In some menstrual cycles the energy travels up instead of down, and nose-bleeds may result, sometimes obviating the period entirely. This is one reason why the contraceptive pill is so dangerous, often suppressing, in some cases entirely, the proper menstrual flow and leading to thrombosis and other circulatory disorders. When the menstrual cycle ceases at menopause, the familiar hot flushes supervene, an expression of congestion within the system in the absence of an habitual outlet.

People with circulatory disease are often overly sentimental and nostalgic and weep easily. This is magnified under the action of heart drugs. It may lead to panic attacks and a fear of going out of the house and meeting others.

The homœopathic remedy NATRUM MURIATICUM is the archetype of negative heart centre expression. Such types are closed and somewhat secretive. They like to be alone and enjoy their own company. Perhaps what is most curious about them is their reluctance to provide genuine reasons or opinions in appropriate situations. It is not a deliberate attempt to hide something they may be ashamed of, as the reasons behind the reticence are perfectly valid and ordinary, yet their curious habit of concealment is unconsciously indulged in, the observer having to employ a high degree of detachment and intuition to discern the layers beneath. However, once the idea is grasped it becomes much easier. They are sentimental, nostalgic and tend to weep a lot; but mostly alone. They will avoid emotional expression as much as possible, especially if highly charged, preferring instead to stamp out of the room and run upstairs in floods of tears. They want others, and want to be wanted, but will seek to establish this without communicating it. They chunter over recent resentments, and hatreds saved up over ages because they were not expressed at the time, resulting in desires for revenge.

Another area of negative heart quality expression concerns the small ego. The heart is where the ego resides and those who are inclined to be egotistical, dominating of others, or even tyrranical, will tend to develop circulatory disease, usually angina. Such people are powerful and therefore often effective but have their power vested in a selfish form of expression and in materialism, often destroying others to gain their desired end. They are, however, good beings in the making and once their consciousness and desire are raised above the selfish level – to embrace the welfare of humanity – then they can turn their mighty power of organisation to the good of all. This is transformation in action; seeing a person for what they may be, and guiding them along their path to greater fulfilment and expression. The quality of the brain depends upon the quality of the heart.

Piles and varicose veins are an expression of prolapse, as is a falling of the womb. It is common amongst smokers and tea drinkers and may be extended towards the heart, the organ becoming relaxed and weak. The falling or prolapsing of organs is usually reflective of a fault in calcium metabolism, originating in poor assimilation rather than input.

Jealousy – or sexual anger – is a most powerful negative emotion whose affect on the heart and circulation is devastating. It affects mostly the left side of the heart and encourages decomposition of the blood. People afflicted by this emotion will also tend to have a high degree of pus and catarrh.

Surgical operations performed on organs directly involving the circulation often have a damaging result on the whole system, including the heart. Removal of piles and the cutting of varicose veins may lead to thrombosis and other forms of ischemia. The production of these maladies is no haphazard affair and reflects faults within the constitution at large, the cure of which lies within (as ever), and is affected most efficiently and gently by the proper administration of homœopathic remedies.

CHAPTER 6

THE LIVER AND SPLEEN

The liver lies at the centre of metabolism and its proper functioning is vital to our health on many levels. The liver controls the amount of blood and energy available and circulating in the body. It is this energy level that enables a person to combat disease successfully or otherwise, and is also a measure of the outgoingness and sociability of the individual. Our willingness and ability to communicate with our fellows depends very much on the condition of this organ.

The liver and the spleen form a balance, with the stomach and pancreas at the fulcrum. Together these organs form the area of direct feelings. We feel the impact of the world here, and the results are distributed throughout every cell of the body. This is the area of passions and desires, and it is uncontrolled activity generated here that reflected on the brain we often call thought.

The liver is the seat within the physical body of the astral vehicle, the vehicle of emotion and feeling. All emotions are registered in the liver and if they are unexpressed, pushed down or suppressed the organ may become congested and its power diminished. Then such illnesses as hepatitis, biliousness, catarrh, coryza, food aggravations, gastro-enteritis and many others may result. The ultimate origin of nearly all disease is from the misuse and lack of control over the astral vehicle of which the liver is the gateway. This is why a negative feeling is always followed by a reduction in energy.

It is the astral vehicle in rampant chaos that creates the craving for such substances as alcohol, drugs, etc.. The physical body does not want them, it is sick of them. In this situation the physical body, in its protective capacity, proves wiser than the person occupying it. This should be pondered on when treating addiction.

Chapter 6

The liver expands under the influence of alcohol, and the individual experiences greater energy as the grip of the vital body is loosened, lessening his inhibitions. This is borrowed energy, and much like money from the bank, must be paid back. In the case of alcohol the paying back will take the form of a hangover, with its contrasting lessening of energy, often accompanied by the congestive symptoms of biliousness, nausea and sometimes diarrhoea.

The liver directly influences energy in all areas of the body, including the brain. The power of thought and the prolonged ability to concentrate and draw considered conclusions on any issue is directly dependent on the condition of the liver and spleen. It is only when the brain is functioning adequately that we can develop the power of forethought. It is through the mind and its material keyboard – the brain – that we make contact with spirit. Alcohol cuts this link, producing a counterfeit experience, and at some point sufficient aggravation so that we may learn to know the difference. It is interesting that we call alcohol 'spirit'.

Too much prolonged concentration is common amongst those whose chosen occupations demand it, and will produce an imbalance in the flow of life with a reduction in the spleen and liver energies, and consequent disease. In this situation attempts should be made to balance the liver by the introduction of physical work into the lifestyle.

The liver has a decisive influence over the function and regularity of the menstrual cycle through its effect over the blood and energy supply in the body. Headaches, conjunctivitis, bloatedness, biliousness, etc. experienced before or during the menstrual period are evidence of congested liver energy. If energy travels up to the head at this time, when it should travel down and through the generative area, creating a healthy menstrual flow, then nosebleeds or congestive headaches will be experienced instead of the period.

During such diseases as hepatitis a dramatic reduction in energy is experienced as the congested or inflamed liver casts a shadow across the whole being. Liver disease is never just localised, it is not of that organ alone, but always to some degree will affect the whole being. The patient is often severely weakened, and may take years to recover. Hepatitis and other liver diseases can remain within the system imprinted upon the astral liver.

Diseases of the liver often afflict those who are emotionally vulnerable, or 'open'. Strong emotion and physical and emotional shock is also known to have a dramatic impact on the liver. The shock makes an impact on the liver via the astral vehicle and causes it to spill toxicity around the body in the form of pus, catarrh, etc., (the physical substance of separation from the self). Hepatitis and jaundice may follow shock, anger or grief particularly in those who are sensitive or who suppress their emotions.

Strong emotions and their suppression also effect the spleen, producing blood disorders such as leucocytosis, leukaemias, anaemias and platelet disorders. The physical response to anger is evidenced by an increased production of white blood cells; those prone to outbursts of anger are said to 'vent their spleen'. Uncontrolled anger freely indulged as a habit will produce this habitual result in the body, and may eventually lead to leukaemia. Anger when suppressed will produce the same result, therefore, anger and its suppression can be said to be a cause of leukaemia.

The liver in its attempts to free itself of congestion, for example, from over-indulgence, will use the joints as a dustbin. Thus the experience of those who indulge too freely is stiffness of joints, muscles (including the heart muscle) and fibrous tissue. Gout is a classic example of this process, with the joints affected terribly. The acupuncture meridian associated with the liver begins in the right big toe, and from there travels upwards. If not properly healed the gouty process will lead to arthritis, and if suppressed will lead to cancer. This is a perfect example of how the body in its wisdom protects vital organs by using the joints as a dumping ground for what it cannot otherwise get rid of.

A congested liver is the cause of much catarrh. This may rise to the head creating the symptoms known as a cold, or it may cause a general and chronic catarrhal condition. Such is the result of over-indulgence, with the frequency of the symptoms depending on the level of the indulgence. Those who habitually indulge will complain of a permanent catarrh, as the liver struggles to free itself of its congested state. The liver may also become congested because of other disease conditions in the body, with catarrh resulting. In this case foods such as dairy products, rich foods and bananas may aggravate the condition by further congesting the liver.

An increase in catarrh may also be experienced under the action of homœopathic remedies, which often stimulate the liver in order to decongest it. During the acute catarrhal process the patient will often complain, thinking himself to be worse. However, this is a positive development, and as much catarrh as possible should be allowed to exit from the body. After the elimination of sufficient catarrh, the congestion will be relieved and a gain in health experienced.

The sycotic process of pus, catarrh and grit will centre on the liver, crippling its power. Gallstones, gallstone colic, biliousness and aggravation from rich food will be the result. The sycotic process will provide the congestion, and may eventually lead to cancer.

The fitter the liver, the more able is the individual to combat any disease. This is evidence of it being the centre of metabolism and a major component of the immune system. Liver disease experienced in life seriously weakens the person and casts a long shadow over the quality of life. The result is often cancer. With patients suffering from cancer it is always necessary to decongest and detoxify the liver. A change in diet is often important. Bowel cancer is particularly dependent on liver dysfunction as a contributive and causative factor.

Influenza is a disease of anxiety and it considerably weakens the liver. The familiar aching of joints during a bout of 'flu' occurs as the liver attempts to rid itself of toxicity. Influenza tends to be either gastric or catarrhal, reflecting two paths of liver energy: through the gallbladder and stomach, or upward to the head producing catarrhal congestion. Generally, the worse the attack of influenza, then the more serious the liver's affliction. This can be seen to be part of the carcinogenic process, and those with cancer have usually had a serious bout of 'flu' in the past.

The liver is the seat of the will, the creative power for action. Without will we cannot act or achieve in the world. Action, the power of doing, is part of the link with spirit. Action is our duty and our karma; not to act is to deny expression to the spirit, and the vehicle which does not fulfil or express itself will disintegrate (disease).

CHAPTER 7

THE NERVOUS SYSTEM

The nervous system can be divided into two areas: the central nervous system and the sympathetic nervous system. They relate in the Bible to the Tree of Life and the Tree of Knowledge.

The central nervous system relates to the brain and spinal column. These together with mind are what is being developed by man as he struggles for greater consciousness in all his present activities and future endeavours. The development of this area also develops the will. During meditational practices the brain is quietened, its habitual activity brought to a stop, whilst the spinal column and the pituitary gland are stimulated in order to receive information directly from the soul into consciousness. This process is usually precluded by the brain's activity, as a clear pool is defiled by stirring the mud on the bottom.

In the Tree of Life the central nervous system is represented by the central column, and the sympathetic system by the outer two pillars. The central column is the balance between the two extremes of the sympathetic system - light/dark, yin/yang, positive/negative, male/female, etc. - the development of humanity seeking the middle path of balance. The more a person prepares themselves consciously in the work of human evolution, the greater will be the spirit's contact with the central nervous system. The spinal column is an energy conductor, and when made available with full consciousness, the spirit will pass as a vehicle of light via the higher vehicles down the spine and through the body, ever increasing the alignment between body, mind and spirit. Energy is also passed between the central and sympathetic nervous systems in this way. The more a person is conscious in the present moment and not dwelling upon past or future, the greater will be his development of the central nervous system, and the ability to align with and serve the spirit.

The central nervous system pertains to the higher mind and the capacity for creative thought. Human beings have not yet developed this capacity for the most part. However, it is for this reason that it is said ARSENICUM ALBUM as a constitutional homœopathic type is representative of the most advanced of humanity so far in general production, for their mind is more developed than in any other. This is illustrated by their ability to think ahead, decide what they want, gather the necessary forces and take action. This may be done selfishly, but nonetheless it is done. The level of self-interest can be worked on later, the capacity is there in the Arsenicum type, while others, unable to decide, think or act for themselves are left complaining about the consequences. They are the prime movers who get results.

The sympathetic nervous system represents the unconscious or habitual nature. It incorporates the ductless glands and the seven major nerve ganglia, together with their spiritual qualities in what is known as the chakra system, the point where spirit meets matter. The sympathetic nervous system is the realm of personality and emotions relating to the small ego or petty self. Our emotional reactions and attitudes activate the ductless glands into passing chemical secretions into the blood; to which every cell in the body must at some time conform. This is the story of pathology, and the cancerous tumour the result.

Continued indulgence in negative habitual behaviour ensures the repeated secretion of the corrosive chemical counterpart into the bloodstream, resulting in disease, decay and corruption. Continued indulgence in an emotion together with chuntering brain activity will cut a groove of habit much like a gramophone record. The overall result is partly why it is possible to read the totality of an individual on the countenance. It is also much in the same way that we may know the homœopathic remedy a patient requires as she walks into our consulting room.

Our unconscious reactions, attitudes and habitual negative thoughts run via the sympathetic nervous system. Living within this system there is little or no control over the personality behaviour. The sympathetic nervous system clouds the incoming spirit, as the dark forest grows its canopy blotting out the light of the sun. This is what is experienced when embarrassment or the prickles of conscience are felt. It is what happens when the individual whose consciousness is firmly rooted in the personality feels 'under attack' from others and starts making excuses or blames others. How much better just to acknowledge the truth and build in the lesson, instead of repeating the habit and going round in the cycle of habitual unconscious behaviour.

Homœopathy as a tool helps the person to cast off the chains of habit by stimulating some consciousness within him of what is going on. He clouds the waters of his mind with his own thoughts of unworthy things and the light of the spirit cannot penetrate. Homœopathy will clear the pool, if but temporarily, allowing some receptivity; and the soul is then able to make some impressions upon the brain.

Habitual activity is imprinted on the vital body through the sympathetic nervous system. If of a negative nature this activity will weaken the power of the vital body both in itself and in its ability to build and maintain the physical vehicle. Notice how negative emotions will destroy energy, and joy and laughter create it; which is why the most important lessons in life are to enjoy it and to learn to love.

It is the polarity between these two systems, one representing the higher self, the other expressing the lower self, and the resulting 'antagonism' from the two states that serves to develop consciousness in man; who is not yet a conscious learner in the field of evolution. We are in our daily endeavours busy building the pathways between the two nervous systems, towards the development of consciousness and evolution. This work, as ever, lies in the ordinary mundane life and not in the great things of one's dreams not yet attained. For the rose to lift her lovely head, the roots must labour in the dark earth. It is consciousness in the present moment, or in other words, doing the job in hand whatever it may be that is required. It is not sufficient to say that you haven't chosen your present circumstances, for on some level you have – if unconsciously. The conscious use of choice will not only focus the individual on the present moment, but will bring into life a faculty which is always there but seldom used; that of free will.

We talk as homœopaths about mental symptoms and their relative value in case assessment and symptom hierarchy. Those symptoms are however for the most part not of the mind but of the emotions, and for the purposes of greater understanding in homœopathic prescribing should be realised as such. The Mind section of any repertory includes such entries as fear, anger, weeping, sadness, anxiety, grief, irritability, shock, jealousy, hysteria, pride, hate, love, etc.. These are all emotional states and are reactions that do not involve the power of thought. They involve the products or reactions of the sympathetic nervous system, the physical adjunct of the emotional body. Those symptoms that really are of the mind pertain to understanding, memory and intellectual capacity.

CHAPTER 8

THE FOUR KINGDOMS

"There are those who speak of their rights when very little is heard about responsibility. Human rights are what masters give to their slaves, freedom is what God gave you."

Humanity as it is today has grown up through three kingdoms of nature, each kingdom basing its development on the achievement of the previous stage. These three kingdoms are the mineral, vegetable and animal kingdoms, and the gifts of each of these are reflected in the fourth kingdom – humanity. This fourth kingdom has only been partially achieved so far, and man really still belongs to the animal kingdom. The fourth stage, that of humanity, as with all fourth stages is a turning point, a change of direction. It is the level where consciousness and matter meet.

Firstly, we will consider the mineral kingdom. Man's physical vehicle has evolved through nature's work, and the bony structure and mineral content of the body are the result of development at this level. The mineral kingdom is the densest matter of the earth, and it is therefore the slowest to change and evolve. For this reason only the highest hierarchies work upon it, and some of the wonderful results we can see in the beautiful crystals and gems of the mineral world.

Nature's work has not always been able to achieve a perfect result, that is to say, perfectly fitting for future purposes. For instance, man's physical vehicle at present is not quite perfectly developed, more work needs to be done to achieve this. The homœopath may play a small part in this process, hopefully, as the conscious instrument of nature. Much like a gardener cultivates his plants, the homœopath needs to work with his patients.

The small physical imperfections we are referring to are the result of mistakes made along the path of evolution during man's development through the various kingdoms. Some of these imperfections are today reflected in the need for mineral kingdom remedies. An example here is the number of babies and small children who require mineral kingdom remedies, such as the CALCIUMS. Childhood is the period of establishment, and proper mineral assimilation and foundation is important for growth and later development. Other individuals may require the reflective metals such as GOLD, PLATINUM and SILVER, all of which reach back in their therapeutic power to mistakes made during the mineral stage of evolution.

It is often good practice to give pregnant women a programme of mineral salt remedies. The early-life requirement for mineral salts begins in the womb when the spirit, via the vital body, is building its physical vehicle from the father's blueprint and the mother's body providing the 'bricks and mortar'. After the birth of the child we may recognise the need for more specific mineral remedies.

The mineral kingdom is composed of dense material matter, and whilst minerals contain tremendous energy and qualities of great healing power, it is the vegetable kingdom that reveals the clear existence of vitality. The plant kingdom follows the mineral as the next stage of evolution. Matter and energy are clearly working together in the vegetable kingdom. This is why plants are observed to react to certain stimuli.

Plants do not have feelings (emotional body), but their energy fields respond to varying conditions of existence. It is the vital force within the plant, under the direction of the group spirit, that causes it to grow and develop. It is the vital body that enables a plant to draw water and minerals from the soil, and to use the sun's rays to create the process known as photosynthesis.

By observing a tree in winter, when there are no leaves to obstruct the complexity of branches and twigs, is to see the great gift of the vegetable kingdom to humanity. Now open a book of anatomy to an illustration of the human nervous system, and there you have it – the development of the root, trunk and branch system repeated in the human body.

The nervous system for man is the physical conductor of vital force, illustrating again the excellence of what we have today that has been built upon the toil of the past. This is a law that runs through all endeavour, whether mineral, vegetable, animal or human. It applies to each generation in the doing of their work, lest the next will be left wanting.

Mistakes and errors committed during the evolution of the vegetable kingdom are met by the plant remedies, which provide the bulk of the homœopathic materia medica. They will be particularly appropriate to diseases apparent in the vital body. This is the kingdom of previous development, mankind at present dwelling in the animal kingdom.

It is in the animal kingdom, built upon the results of the previous two kingdoms, that the passions and desires are born. The astral or desire vehicle is developed here, with its physical counterparts, the blood, heart and circulation, digestive organs and liver. Here we most clearly see the fight for survival as nature develops this aspect. Man is developing mind, but still belongs to the jungle of his own making. Here, hunger, sex and their child fear, have been the motivating forces to which humanity still belongs.

The struggle out of the animal kingdom by the development of mind and the reasoning faculty is the current task of mankind. In our society, if avarice in commercial affairs is all a man pursues, then the forces of mind will use that as a vehicle for its purpose. The raising of self-interest to higher levels of aspiration, and the desire to serve humanity at large, would be a more fruitful route to pursue. Competition has its negative results, it divides and separates, often encouraging the lower aspects of human emotion: suspicion, jealousy, protectionism and finally hatred. On an international level, the source of warfare can be found here; while the forces of evolution seek to create unity and bring together the peoples of the world in brotherhood.

None of us can do anything without first indulging a little

self-interest. It is right that this should be so, as we must work on ourselves before turning our attention to others in the spirit of service. These two aspects, first the one, then the other, are in all human beings, providing polarities and often pulling one against the other – another facet in the development of consciousness.

There will be self-interest in the student of homœopathy as she enters upon her studies. It may be on a level of wanting knowledge, of providing a living for her family, of wanting to know more about herself and others, it may even be wanting to exercise some power over others. It is most likely to be a combination of all these things, but hopefully, underlying all these is the greater quality of wanting to serve others, and this is where the student should find herself once she has graduated and launched herself into practice. Self-interest will govern what we pursue in the world, if this can be raised from the gaining of material wealth to the acquisition of knowledge, then we will have evolved to the next stage of becoming, and out of the animal kingdom.

The diseases of the animal kingdom and its development are met by the snakes, spiders and other animal products in homœopathic preparation. It is interesting to note that these substances from nature often act directly upon the blood, heart and circulation.

In general, the venereal diseases are affections of the desire vehicle and also pertain to the animal kingdom. They are ancient diseases constituting karmic control over the use and abuse of generative power. In homœopathic terms we see here the development of the syphilitic and sycotic miasms. The homœopathic treatment of venereal disease is often difficult, with clear definitions of one miasm over another being somewhat obscured.

The psoric miasm of Hahnemann goes right back to the point when mankind was first required to perform the task of regeneration, the fall from grace depicted in the mythologies of peoples all over the world. This is the most ancient of the miasms and has accompanied man through many stages in the development of his vehicles.

It can be seen how all disease that presently afflicts mankind is a result of the three miasms of Hahnemann. This idea is a working hypothesis, a way of observing a situation. It is not exclusive or conclusive, but to an open mind is an Ariadne's thread through a labyrinth of disease complexities which might otherwise confuse and defeat the observer. There are other ways of looking at the same situation, employing different hypotheses and affording fresh ideas. If one idea is right it doesn't mean that the other is incorrect, but both may be right, providing a different version of the same thing. One may suit one person, the other another person, each working for the good of humanity. We must guard against sectarianism in homœopathy as in every field of endeavour.

The human kingdom is the fourth stage of evolution, God's turning point, and it is here that mind and consciousness descending meet physical matter ascending. Man at this stage becomes a conscious being, balancing freedom together with responsibility to choose his own destiny.

Every human being occupies a physical vehicle, and has a vital vehicle of expression and an astral or emotional body. These have evolved through the three kingdoms of nature, with any mistakes and shortcomings experienced along the path manifesting as symptoms of disorder and disease in these areas. There should therefore be a mineral kingdom remedy, a vegetable kingdom remedy and an animal kingdom remedy for each individual as a constitutional type. There are a few remedy correspondences at present developed that reveal such a pattern; but there is much work yet to be done here. Pioneers with sufficient courage are required to cut new paths and dig deeper into the development of homœopathy as science and art. Too often what is observed is 'very important people' preaching a stagnant stereotype of prescribing, saying that it must be done in a certain classical manner, or that it isn't homœopathy, or that it won't work. Many prescribers claim certain cases are incurable when what is needed is a change in attitude and method of practice; much like the horse seeing beyond his fence the green fields, yet refuses to jump from fear, and remains a prisoner of his own limitation.

The human kingdom is yet to come. There are individuals who point the way, and mankind in general shows signs of what is to come. Yet we are currently only part human and for the main part still animal and quite capable of freely displaying behaviour belonging to both groups.

The lower nature, displaying the characteristic of fierce competitiveness based on fear, still clearly belongs to the animal kingdom. Here we see the source of separatism, divisiveness, jealousy and mistrust that form the basis of war whether on an individual or group level. This is animal man, and it is regrettable that our economic and financial system as presently constituted supports it. Because we are taught that we live in a hostile universe, we accept it as true and assume that somebody or everybody is out to get us. Our behaviour continually reflects this misconception.

We can see love, trust, wisdom and selfless service to others beginning to dawn within the nature of mankind, beyond the expression of the odd individual. Ever more sophisticated communications bring to us the awful sufferings endured by other members of the human family, and with it comes the seed of compassion and the desire to do something about it. We are upon the threshold of our humanity, and what affects one part will affect all the others also. There is a growing desire amongst people to be of more positive service to their planet and their fellow man. This is the beginning of the human kingdom, and let us hope that we can produce those with the vision to see our true purpose and goal.

It has been explained elsewhere in this book how by clearing miasmatic disease from the race we can provide healthier physical vehicles for incarnating spirits of a higher nature. Such individuals will belong more fully to the human than the animal kingdom. The importance of homœopathy in this work cannot be over-emphasised.

There may come a time in human evolution when homœopathy has completed its task. At the present time its ability to root out chronic disease is unsurpassed. In the future, gem elixirs and flower remedies may be the most appropriate natural medicine for humanity, something a little more refined for a more spiritualised being. Certainly by that time the dreadful miasmic and cancerous diseases which today so plague man will have passed. The use of colour and the laying on of hands, used with much good effect in healing today, will probably reach more refined levels of application.

Chapter 8

The bulk of rubrics contained within the mind section of the homœopathic repertory are the result of a chaotic and undeveloped emotional nature, not yet brought under the control of mind directed by spirit. The remedies used to heal these problems will either disappear, or fresh homœopathic provings conducted upon different beings will yield a fresh sympatomatology. Either way, the remedies required for the job in hand will be there.

CHAPTER 9

THE GROUP

The group is a unity, that is to say, an ensemble of units coming together to create a form. The form is the manifestation of the group to which we may readily relate. There is no manifested thing which is not a group or unity, producing a form on a particular level.

The atom is a group of particles, neutrons, protons, etc.. The molecule is a group of atoms; the cell is a group of molecules; each plant and animal is a group of cells. A group of cells produces an organ; a group of organs is an animal or a human being. Each form is a unit and each unit creates the form on the next level up. The life force itself is concerned with the formation and maintenance of groups. It is the basis of all creation, resulting in manifestation, and in the structural principle behind the cosmos, society and humanity.

The success of the group depends upon the degree of integration achieved by the units of that group. Disharmony amongst the units results in dis-integration, decay and death. Herein lies the essence of disease. The life-force has differentiated out from the one (God) to the many manifest and unmanifest forms. The stage of evolution where we are now (the Aquarian Age), requires humanity to form groups. This will happen whether we as individuals (units) are aware of it or not, whether we are willing or not, for in each age the life-force flows in a particular direction carrying all life forms before it. Awareness of this process makes it easier; willing cooperation makes it enjoyable. If we don't cooperate, humanity will be forced to form its groups by nature, and when that time arrives freedom of choice will have long passed to be replaced by fear as a motivating factor.

All this may be observed in the formation of pressure groups in all forms of human endeavour, from trade unions to environmental societies. It is the quality of this group work that reaches not only into the present situation but also far into the future. A group is formed by two or three gathering together around a single idea – the success of the group depends to what degree the units of the group can integrate and give expression to that idea. Our willingness to form groups determines whether we have consultative bodies or all-out sectarian warfare.

The nature of this New Age is that we must live and practice what we believe. The age of proliferation and the spreading of ideas (the Piscean Age), is over. We must now live the many ideas we embrace or believe in. It is not enough to enter church on a Sunday, take bread and wine, later to embrace beer and crisps from a different altar. Lip service is no longer enough, right intention is not enough, only right action will achieve the result; tried and tested in the great laboratory of life. Each individual must put his ideas into practice, interpreting his teaching in daily living, making it personal by virtue of experience and consequently speaking as one having authority. What is heard or read becomes converted into knowledge by the process of life itself.

This is the nature of synthesis, the bringing together of ideas to form a comprehensive overall picture. It constitutes the essence of homœopathy, in which the whole and not just the part is treated, the whole being greater than the sum total of the parts. If one organ is sick then all will require attention. We are taught the power of – and indeed demonstrate in the field of experience – the effectiveness of synthesis as an approach to therapeutics, whilst living in a society whose values are based upon analysis.

The degree of health in the individual depends to what degree the cells, organs and higher vehicles of expression are able to integrate for the good of the whole around a central idea – the purpose of the incarnation. Any dissension constitutes a spreading out from the central idea which binds the group together, a lack of integration, or disintegration. The degree of dissension determining the amount of disintegration. This is disharmony, disease, a diffusion of the individual. The tendency to disunity and disintegration can clearly be seen at work in the sycotic miasm – another force working against the forces of life.

Consider also the cancer cell in this context. The cancerous cell will function in the organ of which it is a part, performing its duties in a seemingly normal way, yet it will be apart from its fellows having interests of its own. It will not fully integrate with the other cells, and it will draw to itself others of 'like mind'. Cancerous tumours are separate anatomical societies that set themselves apart from the interests of the whole, and no longer work for the good of that whole. Some tumours have their own circulatory system (angiomas), and others have their own boney structure (osteomas). In this situation dissent among the members heralds disintegration of the group. A renewal, however, of group purpose from the top of the hierarchy can bring the dissidents back to the common purpose. It has been observed many times that when a person suffering from cancer becomes wholeheartedly enthusiastic or dedicated to a purpose they then find that their cancer has healed. It is the individual who does not fully take up the purpose for which they incarnated (usually through fear), that becomes cancerous.

A society that is not well integrated will produce so much bitter division that some of its members may seek to force their will on the rest by violent means. The country is the body, its people the cells, the terrorist is the cancer cell. The general history of the society is the story of the group spirit's attempt to gain control over its vehicles.

In a sense, disease is like the force of evil that appears in the grand tradition of folk tales and legends from every land. Like the evil witch of the West, it seeks to diffuse the integrating forces of nature, to break down the groups which the great life force seeks to build. So we reflect both: the spiritual forces of nature, ever an upward spiral, forming larger and more complex group forms at each stage towards the ultimate goal of evolution; and also the disintegrating forces of evil, breaking down and dispersing the great spiritual builder. We are at once the princess and the wicked witch illustrated in legend, and so well expounded by today's psychologists – but evidence of the drama does not belong solely to the mind and its explorers. It can be read in detail upon the countenance and within the patterns of morbid physiology so brilliantly displayed by the physical body. Its clamour must not only be heard but attended to by all those who genuinely seek the true healing of the whole being. It cannot be left to those wielding drug therapies. Such treatments are suppressive and will reflect disease up again upon the higher vehicles. We cannot therefore expect disease in the mind to be cured without helping the physical vehicle. Homœopathy traverses both realms, physical and mental, as well as emotional and spiritual, and seeks to restore order to all levels as swiftly and harmoniously as possible.

Study of any one vehicle of human expression will yield much knowledge about itself, but an understanding of the synthesis of all the vehicles is necessary for the observer to have a complete view of the being. From this point of view homœopathic remedy pictures are limited. Knowledge of them is based primarily on provings, together with clinical observations and poisonings. As presently documented they picture the limits of consciousness of provers and observers of the sick and of those who administer to them, and of those who have recorded the terrible poisonings experienced. But there is so much more that exists within these pictures by way of interpretation and analogue, and some people have developed the ability to see these extended pictures. They it is who know that what exists on one level must also be on other levels – this is a universal law. The state of the physical body reflects equally the state of the emotional and mental vehicles.

The point here for the homœopath is one of emphasis in determining the mode of prescribing and the nature and type of remedies to be used. For instance, morbid physiology or pathology on a physical level may reveal a physical vehicle in deep crisis, threatening the continuance of the incarnation. It may be in such a case that the patient will require relatively low-potency remedies which are repeated. Alternatively, disease may be primarily seen on the mental or emotional levels, rather like a physical disease focusing its point of virulence on a certain organ or area of the physical body, whilst the others appear more or less unaffected. Yet we know that all of them are affected, because disease is in truth of all the person and not just a part.

Emotional shock, grief, etc., or out-dated habits, may be more readily observed on the emotional or mental level by the prescriber than their effects on the physical body. Perhaps the mental pathology has not yet descended, or may not do so; it doesn't necessarily have to. This point of emphasis constitutes the discriminating factor required by the prescriber in order to detect the correct remedy. It is what is most prominent at the time the patient consults the presriber, or in other words, recognising the symptom picture and prescribing on it. For illness is not confined, neither are the remedies islands or entities separate and apart from each other – though we study them as such – but they continue on one from another. They form not a single line but a rich tapestry of human error, each weaving its thread in an ever evolving process. The one thread woven closely to its neighbours is what we call the relationship of remedies. The next visit by the patient to the prescriber may reveal a different point of emphasis or symptom picture, the prescriber must be able to discern the pattern as it now presents itself.

Disease on whichever level it manifests can require any potency of homœopathic prescription, so disorders presenting themselves mostly or purely on the physical level may need the highest potencies. This is because the disease is also manifesting on higher levels, it is just not observable at the time.

Learning to interpret the physical body in emotional and mental terms may be a view that some are beginning to take, but very few act upon. Some understanding may be gained as to what is going on in the higher vehicles of expression, perhaps even why, but reflections about physical events tend to be ignored or suppressed by the individual and therapist alike. And herein lies the reason why no action to correct the error is taken; we step away from immediate contact with the physical realm experience, preferring to deal with it in our heads only. Finding out about our mental or emotional shortcomings will tell us much, but nothing will change until we take action on the physical realm, through the physical body. This is the only way to make a change – through effort and experience in the physical. After all, we are incarnated in physical bodies for that purpose; if it were not so, we would exist merely as mind. But we are spirit wrestling with matter through the lens of mind and while the life-force descends, crystallises into matter, that physical vehicle – how we use it, what we do with it – is important. It is the vehicle of our earthly manifestation.

Chapter 9

Psychology, as presently formulated, must make its link with the physical body, and homœopathy must be developed to incorporate an understanding of all the vehicles of expression. Much good work is done by people in total ignorance, who are able to match a symptom picture of a patient with the closest homœopathic analogue. However, this way often fails, and the practitioner through lack of knowledge, is bereft of action, not knowing in which direction to go. He is like a traveller trying to find his way without first knowing where he is. This is how most homœopathic prescribers begin their journey. But it is no longer enough to prescribe in ignorance, we must learn to know what is going on, what is the essence of the patient as well as the remedy.

It is true that the answers to all the questions lie in the remedies, their correct study and observation in action. The realisation that what we read on the page is but a morsel provides the ability to read between the lines and interpret. It is therefore not only what we read that counts but the power of the thought and consideration we are prepared to extend into what we have read. Homœopathy as presently formulated is limited to the existing symptom pictures, with incomplete knowledge as to why or how and little aetiology or prognosis, except by those who have learnt from experience or are able to translate symptom pictures into the living processes of morbid physiology.

There are many unfulfilled areas and questions that remain unanswered, these are the areas in which homœopathy must be developed. One such area is the chakra system with its associated endocrine glands. These are the glands which, through their combinations of activity, do much to shape our personalities and habits, both long and short term. Homœopathic remedies act directly on them, changing their energies and secretions, whether we are aware of it or not. Surely it is better to inform ourselves so that we may be armed with knowledge upon which to act consciously. The ancient Greeks expounded the endocrine system thoroughly, illustrating the processes with stories and giving the names of gods and goddesses to these endocrine secretions. Greek mythology is a highly sophisticated form of endocrinology – for those who can read.

Combination Remedies

The principles underlying group formation run through the whole universe, and apply equally to the concept and application of homœopathic remedies. Many of the remedies that we use are compounds (groups) that form one remedy, for example, CALCAREA PHOSPHORICA and KALI BICHROMIUM. If these compounds are given a Hanhemannian proving or homœopathic picture, they are used as single remedies and we think of them as such. Material science would seek to analyse them, to break them down into component parts in a vain attempt to find an 'active principle'. As herbalists know, it is not always possible to isolate the parts thinking that you can reproduce something the same as the original substance.

It is all the substances together, forming the components of the group, which are capable of producing the effect or group purpose. The whole is greater than the sum of the parts. The isolated substance will be quite different in its effects from that of the whole group.

Dogmatic doctrine amongst homœopaths is almost as endemic as it is in allopathic schools, and many homœopaths put a limit on the same process working in a different direction, namely the use of combination remedies. The fusion of two or three remedies into one produces a new remedy, something which no doubt will display some characteristics of its component parts, but will be a different remedy with a new power. Following the law of the group, its new sphere of influence will be greater than any one of its components.

Those who have used combination remedies, or who prescribe more than one remedy at a time, are accused of poly-pharmacy. If one were to divide the patient into sections, and prescribe one thing for that section, and something else for another, that would be poly-pharmacy. However, this is not what is proposed or intended with this approach. Such combination remedies that do exist have been meticulously worked out. They are remedies that are made by combining substances that have much in common with each other, and through the normal processes of evolution would be the most likely to form the next natural groups in this field.

Combination remedies have their prime use as drainage

remedies. This process is essential in most cases of cancer, which indicates a high degree of toxic material that must be encouraged to drain from the body. There are also other cases which demand this approach. There is little benefit in giving a constitutional remedy if the patient is full of toxic material clogging up their organs and making their energy meridians sluggish. Better to do some work on clearing some of the toxicity out of the way first, before applying the constitutional remedy which will then work deeper, longer and to the greater benefit of the patient.

Combination remedies may also be used as 'organ remedies' to considerable benefit. Organs that are blighted by abuse, not functioning properly, or are congested require support as they may be too weak to take a constitutional stimulation. When pathology has become encrusted upon a patient, the work that is required to improve the condition of the organs may be quite outside the sphere of the constitutional remedy. In many cases giving the constitutional remedy enables the patient to feel better in themselves, but the physical condition remains the same. These are situations where the constitutional remedy is fortifying the patient but not curing them.

Combination remedies can change the diseases or morbid atmosphere of the patient, raising the level of health of the organs and cells throughout the entire body. They can also buy time, in supporting a vital organ such as the heart, which may be so seriously diseased that the life of the patient is threatened before the practitioner can get an overview of the case.

Constitutional remedies often produce their aggravations, these may be quite unpleasant, and may even discourage the patient from continuing with treatment, (for example, with eczema cases). Here, combination remedies, or other support remedies, may be used to assist certain areas or organs for the patient, providing an easier passage towards cure than they may otherwise have had.

Combination remedies can make good intercurrent remedies where they are applicable to the patient, and providing that there is no antidotal or antagonistic relationship to the constitutional remedy that has been prescribed. When a constitutional remedy begins to flag because certain areas of the patient require support, a combination remedy may revitalise the case, sending it on its way again. In this situation it would not be correct to prescribe another constitutional remedy as it would tend to spoil the case, and yet to leave the patient floundering or in discomfort is not necessarily a good thing.

We have, as yet, relatively little information on combination remedies in homœopathy. It is new ground and it needs pioneers. We only find the information by using the remedies, and as for any pioneer, we don't know what it's like until we arrive. This applies equally to the physical world as well as the realm of homœotherapeutics. We must not let this lack of information be an excuse to shrink back from work that needs to be done.

The key to the use of combination remedies is to understand the essence of the new remedy. We must discover its field of influence, power and limitations so that one gets a feel for it, as we do with all the remedies that we use. The process of learning about them is no different, it is applying the same Hahnemannian principles on the next level up. It is not what we prescribe that constitutes the essence of the homœopathic principle, but why we prescribe. Homœopathic remedies are at times prescribed allopathically with something like allopathic results, only the poisoning tends to occur in the higher vehicles, sending the person into dispersion and disarray.

CHAPTER 10

THE ESSENCE OF PRESCRIBING

What we observe is the limit of our observation, what we memorise forms the limits of our understanding. Likewise the patient will report to the prescriber only those conditions which impinge upon his consciousness, leaving the rest to slumber, as it may. What the prescriber does not observe may still be there, yet remain apart from his consciousness. To the 'scientific' mind what you cannot observe does not exist. What they fail to realise is that observation is limited by the degree and power of consciousness, and that consciousness varies from one individual to the next. Our individual consciousness depends on how much we are prepared to be in the present moment, and the degree to which we are prepared to sustain this as conscious effort. Also on this rests the quality of memory.

It is said we must understand the essence of a remedy; more importantly we must seek to understand the essence of the patient.

Human beings are extremely complex and more sensitive than the most sophisticated scientific equipment. We should not therefore limit ourselves to one method or mode of prescribing. Prescribe according to the needs of the patient rather than to dogmas laid down by another. Such philosophies are narrow and will limit the effectiveness of the prescriber.

There are levels of the patient that will know all that is going on, but the patient, with their consciousness seated in the personality, will not necessarily be aware of it. Every level of the individual is active: physical, etheric, astral, mind and spirit. It is well for the practitioner to know a little about all these vehicles and how they seek to relate one to another – you don't have to be an expert.

The Essence of Prescribing

There are three levels of prescribing: healing the sick; creating health; and creating shining spirits.

Although it is not possible to work on one of these levels alone without influencing the others, it is useful to separate them for individual study, as each level may be consciously and deliberately worked upon by the prescriber. Naturally, when prescribing constitutionally all levels are influenced. However, it may be most beneficial to work on one at a time according to the pace and nature of the complaint. This will determine the remedies and potencies used.

Most patients arrive with physical and sometimes mental/emotional complaints, or both. Of course, both will always co-exist, but one may be presented as the reason for attendance, leaving the other to be sorted out by the prescriber when it's his turn to ask questions. There may be an emotional complaint which shows no effect on the physical body, observation in that area presenting everything as normal. However, if permitted to continue, it will only be a matter of time before physical involvement becomes observable.

Healing the sick, therefore, appears to be the most obvious place to start and constitutes the basic requirement of the patient from his prescriber.

The information required to perform successfully on this level forms the bulk of homœopathic teaching and literature at present. Our materia medica, with its sound basics of Hahnemannian provings, paints a subtle portrait of disease patterns, whilst poisonings and clinical experience add the more vivid colours of morbid physiology and pathology.

However, as one level cannot be worked without all being affected, those who are healed by homœopathy are aware of how much better they feel in themselves. This is the great gift of homœopathy, releasing an individual's natural optimistic exuberance and appetite for life, bringing to dominance the more positive aspects of a personality.

This is part of the second mode, that of creating health, and it may be deliberately focussed upon by the prescriber as part of, not separate from, the cure of disease. In this respect it is the constitutional remedy which often fortifies the patient instead of curing their complaint. This is why so many beginners in prescribing will say of a case that the patient feels much better but the ailment remains the same, not understanding why the constitutional remedy failed to do everything. The fact is, constitutional remedies do not do everything, contrary to much misleading teaching. There is an illness experienced by a patient, it may or may not be of a serious nature. The individuality of the patient will give this disease process its uniqueness, as both inhabit the same vehicles of human expression. This disease may have roots and branches throughout the subtle anatomy of the patient and it will almost certainly require more than one remedy to cure. These remedies will enhance the patient's well-being but will remain apart from the constitutional remedy.

It is, though, this constitutional remedy which makes up the bulk of our second idea, that of creating health. It goes deeper into the fibres of the being, increasing the level of health considerably, thus preventing degeneration into the state of ill-health. This is good work with homœopathy and the striking difference can easily be spotted in a truly healthy individual who is beginning to radiate health.

This leads us to the third level of prescribing, that of creating 'shining spirits'. This is the level of consciousness at which homœopathy may be used as a tool for evolving humanity. Sure knowledge of incarnations on a thread of consciousness – like beads on a rosary – provide the long-term point of view. True cure is when the individual is integrated wholeheartedly with the will of his spirit, the personality is lined up with the purpose, to marry the wish and the will and make the brain the servant. When the body, brain and mind are devoted equally to one purpose – that of the will of the spirit – then the person shines like the sun. This is perfect health and a vision well worth aiming for, with homœopathy employed as a developmental instrument. It is no more than the horticulturalist does in growing better and stronger species of plants, yet when applied to human beings somehow the understanding melts away. We are not at the top of evolving life, but a small part of it. There are those who guide us as a farmer might tend his animals; let us hope they have a greater compassion.

This expression of health does not yet exist in our world,

but it will. Those beholders of such a condition would mistake it for an advanced spiritual state, when all it really is is the radiating of a truly healthy individual whose vehicles of expression exist in their natural order, devoid of any perversion. This may be said to be cure.

It does not exist because even its remotest perimeter has not yet brushed the consciousness of humankind. People have not experienced true health, so how could we know the difference? We think we are healthy. Only when the pain and suffering becomes bad enough do we realise that things could be better than they are.

It does not exist also because there are not the practitioners to achieve it! They slumber in what is at present considered acceptable as homœopathy – considering that to be the whole story. Furthermore, in their dogmatic assertions they seek to mummify homœopathy where Hahnemann left it.

Homœopathy as a tool has infinite possibilities beyond curing physical disease, however noble that may be. All it needs is for us to reach out for it. Being conscious of the possibility is halfway to achievement. Practitioners need to develop themselves along more spiritually orientated lines. They are beginning to do this now, providing a vehicle whereby they gain understanding of those who come to them for help and guidance. They need to learn to know the integrity, purpose and direction of another being and whether they may be assisted to achieve it by a swifter means.

The destiny of man is to become nature's tool, spreading and assisting the work of mother nature wherever possible. This does not exist because we simply are not ready for it on so many levels. Let this be a vision for the future, a seed once planted that will one day germinate and fulfil its promise of greater growth.

One aspect of this is that homœopathy means change on all levels and of the profoundest nature. Old habits must be left behind and new, more worthy activities encouraged. But change means making practical use of new ideas, as well as pain and disruption. It requires great persistance of effort. Working on oneself is possibly the hardest task of all but the gain is immeasurable compared with the volume of effort required.

Most disease is karmic, the result of separation from the self –

from a state of oneness – to that of multiplicity. There comes a time in the individual's evolution when it is right for them to be rid of their disease. They may become aware of themselves as evolving spirit in matter, and from then on make some conscious effort to align themselves with the forces of nature, and return to a state of natural integrity. Working with homœopathy encourages this process, and the patient who works consciously with the prescriber is one who will make strides that may not otherwise have been taken. This is homœopathy as a tool of evolution in action.

What the patient observes is the limit of their self awareness. The practitioner should see the patient in terms of what they may be: an odyssey from the grubby presentation to a being powerfully fulfiling the will of the spirit and dedicated to the service of others. This is no imposition of some outside moral code, but the natural fulfilment of one's destiny and purpose through the flow and loving support of life itself. It is not telling others what to do, it is freeing them from the dross of ages, the perversions of aeons, that they might go their way unhindered and with a sweet philosophy.

So how may the practitioner perceive the path of the patient? By observing others in action. What are they really trying to achieve? What pattern is the sum total of their activity likely to impose on their character and personality? Of what lasting value are their activities – beyond the transient insistence of today's demands? What are their needs? In what way do their activities fulfil their needs? What characteristics are they acquiring? What will they take with them when they die that is of lasting value to them as a divine self?

Achievement is gained through action in the world of material manifestation. Everything spiritual has its material counterpart. Everything material has its spiritual interpretation. Could these people fulfil their purpose any easier or swifter? What are they trying consciously or unconsciously to do?

These are just some of the questions the practitioner should ask himself about the patient (and himself/herself), in striving to know the essence of individuality, the spark of spirit from which all else emanates for the purpose of incarnation. Line up the body and brain together, match the wish and the will, adjust to the reality of circumstance, live in the present moment fully with consciousness. These are some of the practicalities on the road back to one-ness.

The first and second levels of prescribing are largely about bringing the patient up to date. This represents a cleansing of karmic disease going back in time. This disease is the sum total of past wrong, separation from self and abuse of the vehicles of expression, including the sexual faculty. Herein are contained the miasms of Hahnemann and all that they represent. They are revealed in various levels of intensity and much work with the nosodes is required here. This is not a process of giving one or two remedies and trusting that the patient will be cured. This is the cleansing of ages and requires much patient work in order that the results be of lasting value.

The great artist does not cast his brush across the canvas creating but a few lines and proclaiming the picture to be finished. He works with his medium, moulding layers of paint one upon another, ever changing the shape and substance of his creation, at first adding this, discarding that, working his picture over and over again until he has bared his soul to the world. The working of a soul through true therapeutic means is no different. What is required here is that the practitioner acquires the depth and breadth of vision, so necessary for moulding the desired result. Make generous use of nosodes, work the other remedies in, take your time, do not hurry, allow the remedies to do their work. The patient has spent many incarnations acquiring ill health, so can now spend a little time and effort in the act of cure.

The patient may suffer aggravations of symptoms, or produce acute illnesses – colds, flus, heavy catarrhs, digestive upsets, etc.. This will be the vitality ridding its vehicles of poisons, toxicity and other morbid matter that represent division, dispersion and disintegrating activity. This is to be looked upon favourably for the patient will be 'cleaner', lighter, more optimistic and generally healthier afterwards. This means the practitioner must have the long-term point of view, be detached – for the patient will not be, and will usually regard such a situation as negative. The patient will complain and demand therapeutic attention. If possible, these aggravations should not be prescribed for.

Continually moulding the patient in this way will in time

bring them up to date. They will be rid of their miasmic disease, and will be noticeably more in the present and able to use the here and now as an effective springboard into the future. They will be more in their bodies, and comfortably so, and their consciousness about themselves and the world will have changed vastly. Negative emotions, depression, fear, etc. will have departed or be much modified, the patient no longer dwelling in their destructive and disabling influence.

At this level the patient may be worked on in terms of their future development to rid them of present habits that may bar the way to the fulfilment of that goal. The patient may report difficulty in achieving some small aim which becomes as a wall barring their progression, preventing them from moving into the next task in their evolution. It is the practitioner's task to observe this, and prescribe accordingly, so that the patient will stop going round in circles, see what needs to be done and get on with it. The patient becomes more aware of where he is going and how best to get there. The alignment of the vehicles is now more fitted for the light of the spirit to shine through. The less worthy aspects of personality, the negative and outlived habits, will wither and die away when no longer indulged in. New and more worthy activities are taken on, attitudes and ideas more suited to today's level of development among humanity at large and better fitting the individual to function to his own fulfilment and in the service of humanity.

While the major constitutional remedies are working, pushing the patient through uncomfortable situations or even aggravations, there is much the prescriber can do to help and guide through the difficulties. The use of biochemic cell salts, intercurrent remedies, and Bach flower essences are several methods the prescriber can use to support the patient without interfering with the passage of the main remedy, allowing that remedy to complete its cycle with lasting benefit. There is a vast relationship of remedies, like a spider's web, on which rest the ebb and flow of life's activity. Through this web we read the nature of life and the relationship of remedies. There are remedies, some of which are intercurrents, that will help and aid the main constitutional remedy and the patient through hard times. This is not prescribing for an aggravation as it is not a deliberate attempt to end the transient suffering but will give strength during that passage, lessening the negative response to the suffering rather than the activity itself. This also prevents the patient falling back into old habits.

The more subtle vehicles of expression are more malleable and therefore respond quicker and easier to remedy potencies, accelerating ahead of the denser physical vehicle. The sufferings of the physical vehicle therefore last longer and often appear more acutely distressing to the patient. It is support on a physical level which is usually most required.

There are many ways to prescribe successfully. Consider for a moment four Nineteenth Century British physicians: Clarke, Skinner, Cooper and Burnett. They knew each other and met to share their experiences and yet each prescribed totally differently from the others, each enjoying great success in the art of healing. Why then do the dogmas persist, insisting there is only one way to prescribe?

It is well for the student to learn as much as possible from as many different sources then to choose a way which is most comfortable for him, expressing his spirit as best he may. What is of greatest value to the prescriber is the patient's report, the remedy having done its work. It is the living evidence of a homœopathic prescription, whatever its nature and outcome. Has the remedy worked and to what extent? What is left outstanding? Has it moved the patient along on their path, served to cure their disease? This report, like the case-taking, is an intimate exchange of assimilable data which is used for the next prescription. It is far more important than anything read in a book or learnt in a classroom.

During the taking of a case dwell less on what is projected onto the paper in terms of symptomatology from patient to prescriber, and the intellectual demand to analyse, but consider more the patient as they are. The integrity as presented. This simple change of emphasis enables the prescriber to reach the essence of the patient. It switches the attention from symptom gathering to observing the patient – a far more important point upon which to focus – and enables the prescriber to better observe the countenance before him, the attitudes and projected atmosphere. It is not what the patient says that is of value, but the way they say it. The PLATINA patient will not complain of pride and arrogance, but observation of his attitudes during conversation will reveal these things. A MEDORRHINUM patient will not complain of being half out of her body, but observing how she forgets what she's saying will tell the prescriber what she needs to know.

What goes on in the brain, what a person thinks, forms their attitudes and responses to the world and others around them. The emotions will respond to what is going on in the brain and vice versa. The response from there will colour the atmosphere which the person cloaks themself with and projects into the world, attracting or repelling. As like is cured by like, so like attracts like, and people draw to themselves what they create in their atmosphere. All our circumstances are the sum total of what we project into our atmospheres by virtue of our emotions, attitudes and idling brain activity.

It is known that sound is vibration. What may not be realised, however, is that vibrations create patterns in the atmosphere (soniferous ether), to which they attract life substance in their effort to crystallise in the world of form, i.e. our material world. "In the beginning was the word and the word was with God", thus begins the creation story. We are in fact creating all the time with our own vibrations.

If the vibration is changed the pattern changes and with it the type of substance it draws to itself. As it gathers substance so it gains weight and form which, if sustained, determines the crystallised form that eventually will manifest in the material world.

Our own world and everything in it is a material result of our own personal vibration. Change the vibration and our world will change. We are the story of our own creation. Our vibration in the world will always draw to it life substance and circumstance. Negative attitudes will therefore draw to them negative results in the world of material experience. Those who are unaware of this process will inevitably blame outside circumstances, not realising that these are of their very own creation. This in turn creates more negative vibration and so the gruesome cycle continues until one day light dawns in darkness, and one intervenes on one's own behalf.

Everything in our life - our job, relationships, home, car, all our activities and their results - is a perfect reflection of ourselves. Better therefore to change oneself than to struggle with the material consequences of one's world.

Those who embark upon homœopathic treatment often experience a somewhat sudden and rapid change of events and circumstances in their lives. This occurs as outdated habits and unedited mental attitudes are rapidly brought up to date in one's evolutionary cycle. The quality of the life improves, problems that have been struggled with for some time will find their natural solution and the individual will grow and make some progress along their chosen path. As the vibration changes and the more positive aspects of the personality are drawn out so will the material circumstances change to reflect a truer interpretation of the individual's changed inner state.

In observing this process we grasp the idea of evolution, providing insights of what is, of what may be, and the road between the two. When this has been observed sufficiently, the prescriber will acquire a 'feel' for it, not only in a general sense, but also for the individual traveller. In this way we may learn to spot the evolutionary line of an individual, immediately knowing what they should be doing with their lives and in what direction they should travel. It is deviation from this that creates disease.

Homœopathy is above all about change, evolution, knowing and understanding. It is in the truest sense of the term our modern alchemy, but this is the Age of Aquarius, it is alchemy for all the people, not just a privileged few. We may all turn the base lead of our gross existence into the pure gold of service, not only for our fellows, but for our own spiritual selves, so that we may shine like living suns.

The Homœopathy of Evolution

There is a growing awareness amongst some practitioners of a deeper and more profound purpose to the homœopathic art than the removal of illness and it is these people who already use homœopathy as an evolutionary tool. The style of prescribing here is different. It doesn't embrace the traditional ideas within homœopathic education that there is one remedy and once given, that's it! In fact, in the author's experience the patient requiring this approach is very rare.

The complexities of disease, certainly in the Western world, go far beyond this concept. The patient will require many remedies, not only to clean up the past, i.e. the sum total of mistakes made and disease evolved through an evolution of millions of years, but to change present-day habits of behaviour linked to that past and which unless dealt with will cripple future endeavour.

We are now the product of all we have been in the past. We are, by our activities, 'choosing' what we will be in the future. Though free choice is a faculty seldom used, yet always present. When we get there, will we want what we have chosen? Or will we cast around, dissatisfied with our lot, seeking to blame others for our circumstances?

Most patients will require a series of remedies according to their habitual behaviour in the various theatres of their life. The nature of habit is repetitive, the individual completing a circle or cycle, repeating the same activity with the same reaction, producing the same result. This is the nature of almost all human life as at present manifested. It is the script unfolding itself, a continuous, unconscious circle of activity. It is the purpose of life to change that circle into an ascending spiral by the addition of consciousness. One of the tools to work that change is homœopathy.

The poverty of spirit at present in humanity is appalling. There is amongst the great mass of people little or no awareness of evolution, spirit, reincarnation, karma or the evolving faculty of mind, upon which we are all at present actively engaged. And yet all these teachings have always existed – even in the West. It is only since the days of Isaac Newton that humanity has sought to explain matter in terms of itself and ceased to recognise the reality of spirit. It is only in the last two or three decades that a recognition amongst some in the West has existed regarding the transfer of teachings from East to West.

In evolutionary homœopathic prescribing we take the long term point of view – what we may be, as opposed to what we are now. This involves travelling from one point to another, which we are all doing anyway, but with this form of prescribing we learn to do it quicker and with more consciousness. We have already stated that there cannot be a poor transmission of a soul, that it is the waters of the mind between the soul and body that become polluted with negative emotional and brain activity. Therefore the suffering individual before the prescriber is in truth a spiritual being capable of shining like the sun, and through the process of life's initiations has the potential to achieve the level of Jesus Christ – the purpose of the Piscean and Aquarian ages together.

The patient could be at any point in a cycle of remedies when visiting the homœopath for the first time. The remedy picture presented at the interview will be the point where the circle is occupied. It will be possible, however, to see the other remedies, or some of them, 'showing through'. One of the remedies in the cycle will be the constitutional remedy, this will act the deepest and will reflect all through the patient's being, but will be best prescribed at the time when nothing else is showing on top of perhaps a more acute nature. One or two of these remedies may be nosodes; nosodes are certain to be required in almost every case.

So the cycle is turned into a spiral, still going round but ascending, as the patient's consciousness reveals to himself the unworthiness of his activities and he voluntarily and by his own efforts makes the changes necessary for a smoother path through evolution.

Change, however, requires endeavour, the keynote of which is diligence. In order for change to become permanent, habits of a more worthy nature and persistance of effort in making them are required. It is so easy to make a token effort with some result, only to slide once again back into old habits. In this respect, the patient will require the same remedy again and again, enabling him to renew his efforts. Prescribers should not be discouraged to see patients slip back into old habits. The prescribing of the remedy produces in the patient a new standard of consciousness, well-being and behaviour. Slipping back again will result in a dissatisfaction with oneself because they have now known and experienced a higher standard. Most people are unaware of this, not having experienced anything other than the way they always are. It is the tension between these two extremes which ever renews the effort to change.

The patient has a taste of spirit, their own. Their life

begins to work well for them. Difficulties are surmounted and new situations encountered. The patient is on their true path, doing what they came here to do, that is, their own work, leaving others to get on with theirs; not influenced by glamour and material values alone.

As the patient evolves so the remedies they require may change. However, it should be noted that each remedy has a higher and lower octave. As we ascend into a more refined state, perhaps the need for Hahnemannian provings of new substances will eventually occur.

In the treatment of disease conditions of the physical vehicle the patient may also slip back into a similar symptom picture as when originally prescribed for. But careful examination by the prescriber should reveal a worthwhile change here, as a reduction in severity and duration of symptomatology is usually observed, indicating that good permanent change has taken place. The patient must however continue treatment in order to reach the point of cure.

For those heavily laden with miasmatic disease, which is most people these days, the disease nosodes will have to be prescribed or it is unlikely the patient will make any permanent change at all. These are karmic remedies enabling the patient to throw off the misdeeds of the past.

A morbid chuntering process will turn a person or illness into malignancy. The brain is a child, being a fairly recent development and requires guidance, discipline and attention if it is to mature correctly. Left to idle on its own it will pick up any morbid matter, turn it over and reflect it out in the life. So what is indulged in during waking hours is absorbed into the being. What is read, the kind of activities we participate in, the company we keep, all have their internal impact and are used by the idling brain twenty-four hours a day, seven days a week. The nature and form of one's physical vehicle is influenced by what the brain chunters on.

The homœopathic remedy NATRUM MUR is closely related to CARCINOSIN and the tendency to cancer. With both these remedies the brain is out of control; it chunters bitterly, resentfully and angrily with a considerable degree of emotional power in it. It is this emotional power which causes the damage. NATRUM MUR and CARCINOSIN often work well together, being frequently interchangeable. Harsh or tragic experiences are absorbed and given little expression or even acknowledgement. Grief is not dealt with so anger and depression are experienced and reflected by the individual. These poison his atmosphere and, in the doing, alienate others and any positive situation which may help him. He therefore attracts more of what he pulls into his atmosphere; like attracting like. He will then blame the external situation for what he feels, thus perpetuating the situation.

In this, as in other situations, the homœopathic remedy will break the cycle, bringing forth a feeling of goodwill and cheerfulness. Imprinted on the consciousness will be the idea, perhaps, that he doesn't have to feel this way, he can feel different, and thereby attracting different things to him. The world has not changed; his view of it has. This then creates fruition – the nature of all growth and change – from possibility to being.

He may sink back into his miserable state, thus requiring the remedy again, but what will have been left is the sure knowledge that he can change. This knowledge is based upon the most intimate personal experience and therefore cannot be denied. Furthermore, once it is known, it cannot be 'not known'. It is too late, the experience is built in and whether conscious of it or not, he will begin in some small way to strive for the beauty of that evolutionary unfoldment, as a plant reaches for the light. The homœopathic remedy reveals his more positive attributes, never giving him anything he has not earned or which is not rightfully his. He must learn to attain it by his own efforts, building in such experience at every stage, the somewhat 'see-saw' experience providing the necessary aggravation to move.

This is the essence of homœopathy as an evolutionary tool, bringing changes in consciousness from that which we are to what we may be. But first we must take full responsibility for ourselves, for who and what we are and consider why we attract to us what we do. The answer is always within, reflected outwards.

Indulgence in activity of a higher quality will produce a better and happier state of being; the attendant consciousness will or should register the difference. But the memory is short, and negative outworn habits are more deeply ingrained than fledgling new ones better fitted for today's evolutionary progress. So beware of the diet on which you feed your brain, it has a voracious appetite. Like most children the brain is quite happy to be left alone and may even resent interference but will co-operate once insisted upon. Many are shallow enough to think that a change in food is the answer to everything. Whilst what we eat is of great importance, the brain has a different diet which is needful of our attention.

CHAPTER 11

THE PRESCRIBER

The patient tends to come with vagueness, it is the prescriber's task to find the specific – the symptom picture, and prescribe the right remedy at the right time. Prescribing on the symptom picture is homœopathy, but so much has to be known in order to achieve this level, all our bigotry and distortions of the truth obstruct the view.

There are four necessary requirements for the practitioner to develop, these are: detachment, observation, memory and respect of truth.

Detachment is the ability to stand aside from a situation without reaction, in order to receive its truth. It is a quality that requires much practice to acquire. It does not mean non-action or lack of interest. It implies a conscious ability to stand aside at will to observe. The body and brain must be quieted – at will – to be free from their perpetual clamour. Meditation is a practice that much enhances this quality through the cultivation of the quiet mind. Part of the art of medicine is masterly inactivity, although allopathic medicine behaves habitually as if in a state of emergency.

Any negative activity of the emotions clouds the mind's efforts at grasping the truth of the patient. Any bias towards the patient, any uncontrolled or unforeseen reaction, however subtle, from colour, race, sex, social attitude, etc., cripples the vision and should be considered as part of an inability to accept another for what they are. In studying the depth of a person it is often found that the external presentation is but a smog covering a worthy essence and distorting their life force – which is much the reason for illness. A good spirit behind a poor presentation.

Keen observation, together with detachment, enhances the ability to know the truth of a situation and act on it correctly. This is separate from the powers of the intellect in 'working out the case'. It is possible to know everything there is to know about another simply by observing one small activity. Ask yourself how much you observe of any situation. It is like saying, "how much of you is in the present?". For the more aspects of you that are dreaming – in the future or the past – or dwelling on something else during the supposed act of observation, then the more you are dead to the truth. When a child behaves in a disagreeable way do not ask her to settle down so that you may take the case; she is the case. What you observe in the first few minutes may be of greater value than the rest of the case-taking.

This is the process required in order to prescribe on the symptom picture, and this is all that is ever required of the practitioner, that he or she prescribe on the symptom picture. It is homœopathy at its purest, simplest and most direct and yet it takes students and practitioners many years to grasp.

To observe with detachment is to assimilate a mass of information in an instant, often contradictory and changeable in its timing, appearance and impact, from which the undulating landscape of homœopathic therapeutics can be applied with precision. It demands of the practitioner that he be fully conscious in the present moment with all his vehicles of expression in harmony.

It is the doom of humanity that it forgets. Again, memory depends on the practitioner's ability to be in the present moment. Any daydreaming means that the consciousness is not alive to the moment, the information to be remembered is therefore not received and is missed. Like any other faculty, memory can be developed by being used and worked upon.

If memory was all that it could be, we would carry with us perfect access to the contents of previous incarnations and what went on in between. Thus with memory comes the knowledge of immortality; that it is only the physical body that dies. Thus we grope for truth in the darkness, a true wilderness for the children of the earth. Who can remember what they were doing this time ten years ago, or even two weeks ago?

During the homœopathic interview the patient's memory and ability to organise the mind may be observed first hand. There may be no need to question, it is there to be observed. Many are so disorganised that they may remember little between this and the last interview.

"Shatter your ideals upon the rock of truth"

The truth is what is; unassailed by opinion, feeling or intellectual philosophies of convenience emanated by the brain and sympathetic nervous system to bolster a status quo, or otherwise pervert much needed change.

The patient will always have 'reasons' or excuses. Our society is propped up upon excuses and other very good reasons and in doing so we support each other in our weaknesses. We blame external circumstances to justify ourselves so that we don't have to make a change in ourselves; it is somebody else's fault and therefore we are not at all to blame. In doing this we surrender our power.

Can we respect the patient for what they are yet realise their weaknesses and remain uncritical? Can we revere the higher nature without being scornful of the lower? The truth hurts, it means we make mistakes, we are less than perfect.

We need to develop the ability to comprehend the very essence of a situation, stripped of excuses and specious reasons, to see it for what it is, with detachment. We must hold this as an ideal above all else, however much it may hurt. People will not curse you for your weaknesses but will curse you for exposing theirs.

The basic requirement of detaching oneself from any emotional involvement with the patient, their story, or one's potential reaction thereto, is the beginning of the ability to penetrate by direct cognition the wondrous simplicities of another, without adding opinion or feeling. This does not involve the intellect in any 'working out', but is the faculty of direct knowing. In prescribing, endeavour to perceive the patient as they are and not as a collection of symptoms projected by them onto paper for intellectual analysis.

A patient will have a cycle of remedies according to their cycle of habitual behaviour. We all have habit patterns, mostly undesirable, which we tend to repeat largely unconsciously in a cyclic manner. A given stimulus resulting in a certain habitual line of activity. These habits are reflected as substance in the vital force or aura of the individual. Disease – family and ancestral – vaccination and drug related disorders add to the substance of this habitual activity, any change being all the more difficult. Homœopathy releases these 'phantom forms', enabling the individual to take on change naturally as the next logical stage of development.

This cycle of behaviour forms the ebb and flow of the person's life and at some point during this cycle they may seek homœopathic assistance. There is a homœopathic remedy for each stage of the cycle, say about six or seven in all. The prescriber's task is to identify at what stage the patient has arrived, and to seek out the corresponding remedy. Such a prescription will push him round the cycle, gradually increasing his consciousness at each stage and changing his behaviour to something a little more ennobled and refined; fitting him more for what he should be doing in life. Thus does the cycle become a spiral, and as with all life, he rises towards the light, moving and evolving but more consciously than before and with some direction of purpose.

One of the remedies in the cycle will be the constitutional remedy, which is usually better at fortifying the patient than curing them. It is not always the case that the patient requires the same remedy in ascending potency, as is often taught. The danger here is that the prescriber, having found what he considers to be the remedy, will go to sleep on the case and lose touch with it. Very often a remedy is prescribed and the picture then changes, bringing the patient to the point where they need the next remedy. As a person evolves, so they pass from one stage to the next and the picture changes. Also there is so much karmic disease to consider, prescribing on aetiology and bringing the patient up to date.

In prescribing like this it is important to see the patient regularly, as remedies tend to work no longer than six to twelve weeks and the patient quickly passes to another phase which requires acting upon. In this way the patient evolves. It may not be necessary to prescribe at every interview but there is no waste of opportunity for the prescriber to learn more of his patient, and there is always more to learn. Human beings are complex and function on many levels; it is not possible to find out everything at the first interview.

The remedies in the cycle may change as it develops into a spiral. New ones are introduced, revealing a line of development through a chain of remedies, for example, from NUX VOMICA to ARSENICUM. Each remedy a signpost through an evolutionary process, each one revealing its own power of development relevant to the individual.

Most disease is the result of past mistakes made along the path of evolution. Homœopathy can wipe out most of the consequences of past mistakes, and in the doing, change the course of the future as old habits are broken and no longer indulged in. It does, however, take a lot of perseverance to break these old habits completely. This may account for the situation where the patient is doing well and then it all stops. Homœopathy brings the out of date habits fully to the conscious mind, giving the patient the opportunity to work at changing them. The stronger the will the further it will carry them.

Past weaknesses are old habits which were of use in the past, but are no longer required. They do not now nourish or sustain the life but have become woven into the fabric of the present. Homœopathic treatment will reach into the past disposing of the dross of ages. The action of some remedies is particularly useful here in reaching into the past. THUJA is one such remedy, it is not dramatic in its action, yet if observed closely it can be seen to reach deep into the shadows of a person's past, correcting much error made upon the way. This is in contrast to, say, NITRIC ACID, a close relation of THUJA. The action of NITRIC ACID is more dramatic and relates directly to present activity in the patient. If the observer can at once perceive the difference between the action of these two remedies, then there will be the beginning of penetration into the evolution of a soul.

It is working in depth with a patient that is so important. Learning and knowing the remedies is important but so is discovering the complexities of humanity and its myriad deviations.

Observe and remember, play with ideas and speculate on them. Consider new ideas and use them in practice or they will grow cold. On coming across a new idea (possibly from another person), do not cast it aside because it does not fit into your present comfortable habit of thought. The brain will always choose Barabas. Neither must you accept it without question, like a sheep. Play with the idea, consider it, relate it to what you already know from your own experience. Do not scorn the source of your information – great revelations come from unlikely places. Be open minded.

When prescribing learn to 'feel' the atmosphere of another, be aware of it. How does it make you feel to be in the company of this person? What is going on inside you? It is possible to know a constitutional remedy by feeling and realising the quality of atmosphere of another. The brain will intervene and block the intuition – "it is impossible because it's not logical". Our society makes itself dependent on the brain and its products. It is interesting to get the brain out of the way and find out about other parts of oneself.

Know that man is a spiritual integrity and not a piece of mobile protoplasm, which is what the darkness of the world would have us believe. Know something of his various vehicles of expression, rather like a camera with many lenses. The accuracy of focus determines the clarity of image created on the paper by the light of the spirit entering the opposite end.

When we criticise another we justify our own position from which we do not wish to move; so we may feel safe. Feel what it is like to be in another's shoes and know from your life experience how it is to go through what another is experiencing. It is so important in homœopathic prescribing that our own experience of life is rich and varied so that we may empathise with others, and also understand, because we have been there ourselves.

When we follow the current forces of evolving life, then we flow with them and they with us. Then there is no disorder, no failure; the mistakes of a child learning, yes, but no more than that. The universe is supportive of those who work with it. All that is needed will be provided, as and when it is needed, while humanity makes provision for disaster. We are blind and wishful of things that are not rightly ours so when provision is there we do not see it under our noses. We pass coldly by and wander in the wilderness wondering why life has become difficult.

Homœopathy is in line with the current evolutionary forces, and growing as a consequence. It is now a fraction of what it will be. There is a great need and those who are truly needful are guided. For this reason it is well to go forward unafraid with the courage of our own convictions. Stay with the quality of pure aspiration, the original impulse to serve one's fellows, and not the blind need of materialism.

In moving into our New Age a new hierarchy is required to replace the old. The old system of position by privilege is being replaced by one of ability. Therefore all one has to do, in whatever field of activity, is be effective. One does not require favour from others, or paper qualification, though both may appear attractive and desirable. What is required from each of us is our commitment of service to contribute to the whole.

To consider oneself not yet ready is a question of pride. We are ready when we are sought by others and the patient arrives at the front door. They are guided to the one who has what they need. It is our duty to provide when others are needful. We don't necessarily consciously know what it is that they need, but if given the opportunity they will receive.

The patient will have arrived at the homœopath's door by a process of thought, deduction and right feeling (sometimes confused with intuition). He or she will know that this is the next move to make. This is why it is unwise to 'fish' for patients, or to advertise in any shape or form. By affinity will the selection of a particular practitioner be made, the practitioner drawing to him what is rightfully his.

There are those who approach the practitioner with themselves much to teach. The detached observer will know and receive the word. The patient will always reflect an aspect of the practitioner, acting like a mirror to his own situation. The patient is drawn by ties of loyalty and love whose roots lie deep in the past, and should therefore never be turned away by the petty self-indulgence of a practitioner who may not think himself 'ready' to practice or take this case.

It is not easy to be a practitioner. There is difficulty when moving into new areas of endeavour. But those who wait to know will never know before they fade out. Knowing comes from experience, and to know homœopathy, it must be practiced. The universe is not harsh with those who choose to be creative and act on their ideas, but it is with those who sit on the fence and remain inactive. The point of power is now; it is the only moment we have to do anything.

In our striving to be effective we create a hierarchy of ability, those knowing more passing their knowledge to the student who knows less. And in the act of passing on our knowledge to others, so we are able to receive more ourselves.

CHAPTER 12

GONORRHOEA AND SYCOSIS

The mutation of disease is an interesting study provided the observer is aware that the same disease may have a variety of different disguises, much like a friend wearing different sets of clothes. When this is not understood, each stage is identified as being totally separate, a different disease with a different source of 'infection'. Disease will mutate through the generations, and within an individual depending upon the habits of the person and any medical treatment received.

Gonorrhoea is a disease with a thousand masks, and not all of these have been lifted to be recognised. It is most obvious at its point of inception, which is usually, but not always, through sexual contact. Once activated it sets up an inflammatory condition in the genitals and a pussy discharge, whereupon the individual usually seeks medical assistance. Once antibiotics have been administered, the disease is suppressed and driven deep into the being where it becomes ever more subtle.

In the male, gonorrhoea shows as a urethral discharge accompanied by inflammation and pain on passing urine usually identified as cystitis. It is quite rare for males to produce cystitis, and this is most often from gonorrhoea. The use of antibiotics for these symptoms may drive the inflammation inwards and upwards, past the bladder and to the kidneys where nephritis may threaten. In females, a discharge ensues, this may go unrecognised and will eventually lead to a virulent salpingitis. Again, cystitis is likely to develop, with again the risk of driving it up into the kidneys with the use of drug therapy.

These symptoms so far are easily recognisable, however, that is often as far as the understanding of gonorrhoea goes, the rest is 'secret'. Orthodox medicine regards gonorrhoea as an infection by the gonococcus microbe, and when this is exterminated, the disease is said to be cured. Sometimes the active disease symptoms are slight, other times the symptoms are dubious in their nature and may be labelled as non-specific urethritis (NSU), or herpes, but these most certainly spring from the same source.

In truth, gonorrhoea by its very nature may vary in virulence, because it is a quantity of something, an amount. It is much more than the presence of a gonococcus. In fact, we can see that mutations exist producing symptomatology of the disease, without a gonococcus ever being present.

Of what is gonorrhoea an amount? It is the product of, and produces, three things: pus, catarrh and grit. Of these, pus and catarrh are the same thing differently expressed. Grit is created by all the venereal diseases, and the crystallising tendency leads to tuberculosis, gallstones, kidney stones and arthritic diseases.

In its chronic form gonorrhoea will strike in upon the constitution of the individual producing disease, decay and corruption on every level. Each stage of this disease of disguises, when not recognised by medical observers, will receive a different diagnosis and label. The use of antibiotics and other suppressive drugs will render it ever more subtle and difficult to recognise, and then from time to time it will reveal itself through an acute or subacute phase, often again to be suppressed by drugs and eventually likely to express itself as cancer.

It is this 'striking in', or manifestation of the chronic form of gonorrhoea that in homœopathy we call sycosis, or the sycotic miasm. The disease will mutate in the person who had gonorrhoea originally, and if he or she should have children, it will reveal its stamp upon them also. Gonorrhoea casts a long shadow down the generations, and will eventually work its way out after six generations, providing no fresh contributions are made. A second contribution in the same person, for example, if that person was under the illusion that the first dose was cured by antibiotics, may lead to tuberculosis in that person or their children. If both parents have had gonorrhoea, then their offspring will almost certainly produce either tuberculosis or cancer.

If we are aware of these things as homœopaths it is possible to clear the disease out from the individual in one generation, so that the patient, or their child, does not get the cancer or other chronic disease they were heading for.

It is an understanding of the process of synthesis that creates a good homœopath, the realisation that various diseases are the offspring of a parent disease. Synthesis is a law of evolution; a group working together to produce the fruit on the next level up. Medical science as presently constituted does not recognise this process, but divides, sub-divides and classifies everything as a separate disease, whose aetiology is unknown or due to 'infection'. This system is devoid of understanding and is unnecessarily complicated, leading to people becoming more sick and not better.

This is fundamentally why our national health service fails, not because the ideal itself is misplaced, but because medical understanding and the subsequent system of therapeutics doesn't work. Modern medicine was born from war, and it is a fact that everything in existence carries with it the spirit prevailing at the time of its creation. Everything in the seed will be carried forth to the plant and the subsequent fruit. It can thus be seen why everything in our medical system, including the process of birth itself, is treated as a serious disease or potential emergency. Fear is the weapon that spreads dependence on the system amongst the people.

We shall now trace sycosis through its various forms from the acute gonorrhoea, or urethral inflammation, to its conclusion as cancer.

In homœopathy the condition known as sycosis is synonymous with sepsis because the same putrid conditions may be found with or without the presence of a gonococcus. The homœopathic remedy MEDORRHINUM, a nosode made from the gonorrhoeal discharge itself, when studied tells a long story of putrefaction. The study of sepsis is one of the most important subjects for anyone in the field of medicine. Unfortunately, it is so often overlooked in favour of infection, and then interpreted as a bacteria or virus to be destroyed whereupon the patient is considered cured.

Sepsis is another word for pus, and pus is synonymous with catarrh. When pus crystallises it forms grit. It should now be easier to see why sycosis, whether from active gonorrhoea or any other cause, is a quantity of something; and the human race is full of it! It is important to fully grasp this when attempting to heal a patient who is full of poison. It is a truth that has been discarded with dangerous consequences since the science of bacteriology was born around the time that Koch first discovered pus in the blood in 1876.

When certain microbes are destroyed with the use of antibiotics and other drugs, the pus or putrid process is ignored and left to decompose the body further. How can this be considered a cure? So many of our diseases are the result of pus and catarrh being present in the body; and most of these will have their roots planted in the sycotic miasm. Thus we have described the source of the diseases we know as typhoid, pneumonia, malaria, tuberculosis, bronchitis, arthritis, tonsilitis, appendicitis, asthma, eczema, endocarditis, otitis media, all catarrhal conditions, etc., etc..

From time to time the body in its wisdom will attempt to throw off its toxic burden, and in so doing will create an acute manifestation of disease. Many of these will obviously indicate the presence of pus, such as, tonsilitis, abscess, mastoiditis, etc.. If the pus is allowed to pass from the body without suppression the patient will feel great benefits in their health after the acute episode has passed. However, often the sepsis is driven in with suppressive drug therapy, the body's vital initiative is thwarted and the immune system damaged. It is not realised that the physical body has an intelligence of its own and will often settle the matter if allowed to deal with it.

When the pus is driven into the body, it may at some time seek another exit in the form of an abscess or whatever, or it will settle to become a chronic constitutional blight which will cripple the patient's expression of life for good. Most of humanity is in this state, so who knows the difference? Those who have had years of homœopathic treatment do, and so do those who treat and observe them.

After a number of years of low level sepsis and putrefaction within the body the conclusion is drawn that is cancer. Cancer is the result of morbidity and mismanagement of disease, of which pus (sycosis), is the prime physical cause.

Vaccination adds to this process. An inoculation is pus injected straight into the blood. If worded like this it becomes unattractive as a market manipulator and people wouldn't like it, but pus it is; and more and more of it is poured into our children's bodies every day. When this is added to the pus already present by inheritance, and when it is suppressed by antibiotics when it attempts to exit, and then not forgetting the increased amount of venereal disease that has accompanied greater sexual freedom, it is not surprising that we have the most devastating time-bomb ticking away in us all. This sorry state we have projected outwards as an anxiety of nuclear war, but outside us it is not; it is within us, as ever under our noses. It is the set-up for cancer, which we wonder why we get, thinking that it is something that jumped on us by mistake. There is no such thing here as an innocent victim, only ignorance and its consequences.

The greater the suppression of the septic state, the earlier cancer manifests, until it appears in the very young. Moreover, the enormity of this burden has damaged our immune systems so severely that it is hardly surprising that AIDS is upon us; the origin and causation is obvious.

Sycotic Symptomatology

The sycotic miasm may be recognised in an individual by a general marasmic state. The young person becomes pale and with a waxy complexion. They are easily exhausted, irritable, crave stimulants and perspire easily on exertion. They begin to suffer with stiffness of the joints.

In the woman there may be the most terrible inflammations of the reproductive system. Salpingitis with severe pain may develop. There may be very painful periods and also ovarian pains experienced at the time of the periods or at ovulation. These ovarian pains are sharp and agonising and soon cysts will grow on the ovaries. Sycotic women are prone to all sorts of menstrual problems. They may also lose all sexual desire and become very nervous and subject to violent outbursts of temper.

The sycotic person can become nervous, tearful, fearful and hurried. This may develop to the point of paranoia. It is a disease that gradually takes over the whole body and dictates terms of existence to the occupant.

Chapter 12

Sycosis is the fig-wart disease of Hahnemann, and genital warts are often seen to develop. These are usually swiftly suppressed to the great detriment of the patient. It is fashionable today to speak of the 'wart virus', which creates warts on the cervix and vagina and is believed to lead to polyps, fibroids and other morbid changes in the cell structure of the cervix. It is not the virus that is the culprit but suppressed gonorrhoea that is being passed amongst the population. There may or may not be a gonococcus, or other beastly 'invader' to be found, but the disease in its entirety is not dependant upon one small organism.

Along with generative disorders, kidney and urinary disease are commonly sycotic, resulting in inflammations and degeneration of the kidneys. Bright's disease is another feature; it is the pus that sets up the inflammation and degeneration, and grit provides the stones in the kidneys. The sycotic patient's urine becomes thick and yellow, with sandy deposits and analysis will reveal the presence of pus.

Cystitis may be frequently recurrent in the sycotic person. There may be found a measure of virulence here, with a mild sycotic taint mirrored in a cystitis of slight inconvenience to the sufferer. However, a large amount of pus in the body may set up a urethral inflammation of such severity as to be exceedingly uncomfortable to the patient, rendering them unable to function properly. The pain of this cystitis may be described as 'passing glass', and is usually either directly a gonorrhea (suppressed with antibiotics), or dependent on some outrageous sepsis having been suppressed in the patient, such as typhoid. The suppression of this cystitis will result in kidney disease.

Sycosis may follow a route from the generative organs and kidneys, through the body to the liver and gall-bladder. Here gall-stone colic and other inflammations involving an excess of pus, grit and catarrh will result. A congestion of the liver may develop; a serious development in the overall health of the individual. Bilious attacks may be present, with the liver using the joints as a dustbin for pus and grit. As the degeneration continues, a crippling arthritis may result. Arthritis and rheumatism are sycotic diseases.

Sycosis is also a disease of the blood. Its festering nature will change the composition of the blood, producing anaemias, platelet disorders, leucocytosis and leukaemias. In treating sycotic and cancerous patients with homœopathy it is important to regularly use remedies that clean the blood, as otherwise the blood disorders mentioned may develop, or the depositing of poison into the vital organs may lead to inflammatory heart disease or cancer.

It may now begin to be clearer why this disease affliction is not a virus, but a quantity, by virtue of the varying symptoms observed in different patients. Pus is the primary expression of gonorrhoea, followed by catarrh. In truth, there is little difference between pus and catarrh although with active gonorrhoea there may be more pus, and in subsequent generations there is more catarrh.

Pus as a primary factor in the equation invariably means that the lymphatic system is heavily involved. It is observed that rashes of a gonorrhoeal nature appear in areas of the body where lymph glands are present: in the groins, axillae, behind the knees and creases of the elbows, etc.. Eczemas are often found in these areas, and to use ointments on them is to drive the poison back into the lymphatic system. A continuous pussy presence or discharge in the lymph system is a very likely set-up for cancer.

The health of the lymphatic glands are an indication of the general condition of the blood and the body. Whilst their temporary swelling with little nodules is a sign of them doing their work, a chronic or repeated swelling is a sign of high toxicity of the body, and must be dealt with properly if the patient is not to develop more serious degenerative disease later on. The tonsils are part of the lymphatic system, and their repeated inflammation and swelling, often with pusy deposits, is an obvious indication of the state of the body in general.

To suppress tonsilitis with antibiotics, or even worse, to excise them with the knife, is a brutal denial of the body's natural intelligence. There is a link between the ears, nose and throat on the one part and the kidneys and generative organs on the other. They develop from linked cells in the embryo, and energy flowing through these areas is the same energy, but with two expressions; a higher and a lower octave. The generative organs, of which the urinary organs are a part, are those of creative expression on a lower level (lower here does not mean inferior). The throat, of which the ears and nose are a part, is the area of higher creative expression; speech, music, art, etc.. It is common that those individuals with a high creative and artistic ability often have an equally high sex drive, reflecting a degree of creative energy with its two-pronged expression.

A patient suffering with repeated sore throats is likely to also have some generative or kidney disorder. The removal of tonsils from the throat will drive the disease expression inwards and towards its other area of expression, the kidneys and generative organs. This may result in prostate dysfunction, nephritis, or menstrual disorders and the production of polyps, fibroids, cysts, etc.. The time lapse between these events may be short – weeks or even days – in which case a connection may be made in the mind of the sufferer; however, should the time lapse extend to months or years, no link will be made and the aetiology will be declared unknown or a chance 'infection'.

When the sycotic process moves to the head, it will produce migraines. These may be worse for eating chocolate and cheese, and will produce visual disturbances and bilious vomiting. There may be a pussy discharge from the eyes and a tendency to inflamed eyes. There will be abundant wax in the ears (catarrh and pus), and a discharge from the ears that may excoriate the outer parts. Gums will be soft and bleeding with pussy pockets and a soreness of the mouth.

Gonorrhoea is the disease of excess, of over-production; and here we should note the Twentieth Century obsession with material production. Gonorrhoea begins with an over-production of cells on the physical level – warts, polyps, fibroids – and if the patient has a morbid mentality leads to cancer. It is a disease expression that permeates the higher vehicles, and creates an excess of expression in the emotions and mentality also. The individual may become obsessed with accumulating money as the end to a means, rather than producing enough for a particular purpose. Great satisfaction may be gained from the display of excess wealth in front of others.

Mentally, the sycotic patient is 'detached' from life. Life seems unreal to them, as if observed through a dream. In modern terminology they are 'spaced out' or unearthed. It is so that their vehicles are not fully integrated; they are not properly in their body. This leads to an inability to run the practicalities of their day-to-day life successfully, they do not have a sufficient grip on reality. Many who smoke cannabis are like this, and it is interesting to note that CANNABIS as a homœopathic remedy is used for treating some cases of active gonorrhoea.

Diffusion is a keynote of sycosis, with the inner state reflected in the outer world. It is a condition that may lead to uncontrolled psychism and clairvoyance. Sycotic persons are indecisive, of two minds. In the homœopathic remedy THUJA, this may be described as a devil and an angel attempting to persuade the patient first this way and then that.

The sycotic person is never able to find an inner harmony, being constantly in a state of flux or conflict. Reflected in the life this may become the 'triangular' relationship, in which a husband or wife takes a third party outside the marriage. This situation is a diffusion within the emotional life, in which he or she is unable to give their intimacy to one, but must create duality upon the one purpose.

The greater the poison or pus (sycosis), within the body, the more unearthed and diffused will be the person. Some children are so full of pus and catarrh that they are not in their body's at all, but just sit and stare, not able to respond when addressed. They are often regarded as mentally sub-normal, when really they are only sick, and with proper care and intelligent medical treatment they may be cleansed and enter their body and their life more fully.

The sycotic person may express his condition by the possession of two houses, two or more cars, and a multiplicity of goods which they want now, or irritability and even violence will result. The continuous accumulation of money and possessions far beyond that which is needed will provide a chaotic lifestyle appropriate to a diffused individual. The process of diffusion on a group level has largely created the society that we live in, and its monetary system based on debt.

The strongly sycotic remedies, such as, THUJA, PYROGEN, BAPTISIA, PETROLEUM, etc. all have a duality or diffusion in their picture. They also all have varying degrees of pus and catarrh.

The nature of diffusion is a spreading out, or breaking down process; the opposite to the state of synthesis in which the group on one level provides the point for the component on the next level up. Thus, sycosis is anti-life and anti-evolutionary. It is a definition of disease within humanity, seeking to destroy the very substance of life and the development of mankind.

The Sycotic Child

The children of gonorrhoea inflicted parents are often small and emaciated. They quickly produce chronic catarrhs and asthma. The catarrh may be thick and green, or yellow when there is pus present. The sycotic child may have frequent colds and these will often descend and become a cough or bronchitis. The tendency to bronchitis is a distinguishing factor from TUBERCULINUM, as it is MEDORRHINUM which has bronchitis. From bronchitis, pneumonia may develop, which is a disease that depends on a high septic state being present in the patient.

Sycotic babies are born with sticky eyes and have periods of thick pussy eyelids that get gummed together. These eye symptoms may be mistaken for or described as conjunctivitis. The babies have cradle cap, or develop eczema of the scalp and elsewhere on the body. Eczema is a catarrh of the skin.

Asthma and eczema complement one another, they are two ends of the same stick. If the eczema is driven into the body by suppressive applications, such as steroid ointments, so will the asthmatic tendency become aggravated. True healing takes place from above down, and from the inside to the outside. The skin is an organ of elimination, and any application on its surface will drive a disease manifesting on the skin into the body and the vital organs. In the case of suppressing eczema the disease process invades the lungs and bronchi resulting in asthma and in an overall deterioration in the person's health and well-being.

The navel of the baby may be slow to heal and may even suppurate, revealing the unmistakable passage of sycotic disease from parent to child. The placenta may have pussy deposits or pockets in it when examined after birth. The infant may suffer from severe 'nappy rash'. The skin around the genitals and anus becomes fiery red and looks scalded, and may even slough off. This may or may not cause distress to the infant, but it is a mistake to apply medication to the surface as it is not a nappy rash in the normal understanding of the term, but is a gonorrhoeal rash revealed on the skin in the genital area, for which the disease will naturally have the greatest affinity.

The nappy rash may have extensions in the groin and axillae. Sometimes lipomas (small fatty deposits), may be observed in the parts of the body where the lymph glands are found, and especially in the groin.

Sycotic children can develop pain on passing urine. Adults with sycotic cystitis will describe the pain as like passing glass, but the children cannot describe it. The child's experience of the pain causes them to scream when the desire to urinate is felt, and results in them attempting to hold the urine instead of passing it. Eventually, after much distress, they have to urinate, which will cause more screams of pain. They may also have constipation because pain on passing a stool causes them to hold onto it. Once recognised it is fairly easy to make a diagnosis and will require the gonorrhoea remedy MEDORRHINUM to bring swift and permanent relief.

The sycotic child's general behaviour and temperament is often apalling. Rapid changes of mood from being affectionate and clingy, to raging violence are experienced. To the observer, the suddenness together with the extremes of behaviour, are a clear giveaway of the diagnosis. It is the mother who experiences the child's worst behaviour, being on the receiving end of what started as a dream fulfilled and rapidly turned into a nightmare. Others may find her offspring well-behaved, although violence and cruelty directed to other children may also be observed.

Waking in the early morning is a common tendency with the sycotic child. It is said in homœopathy that being worse at night is syphilitic and worse in the day is sycotic. This can be misleading, as the sycotic patient may well be worse during the night, although this will usually be confined to the early a.m. hours.

The appetite of the sycotic child is usually poor, and they tend towards junk food, especially those high in sugar and salt. Cheese and sweets are particularly desired, as are oranges, orange juice, vinegar and strong-flavoured or smoked foods. The bowels are often prolific, producing diarrhoea with an explosive, spluttering stool. There may be urgency and pain. For babies and small children, as well as for adults, the bowel is a route of elimination.

Because gonorrhoea is a quantity, an amount that has to leave the body before cure can be said to have taken place, correctly prescribed remedies will often cause an aggravation and a rapid change in symptomatology from the chronic to an acute phase as the body gathers its forces of regeneration. This will be a tell-tale sign of a favourable physiological process taking place under treatment. What may seem to be severe colds will appear with much thick green or yellow catarrhal discharge. Coughs with an expectoration, a profuse and offensive stool, boils, spots, whitlows, etc. are no haphazard affair but are the result of the body's natural intelligence ridding itself of unwanted matter.

Gonorrhoea and Cholesterol

Cholesterol is a fatty substance found in bile. Bile is composed of water, mineral salts, mucous, lecithin, bile pigments and cholesterol. It is secreted by the hepatic ducts of the liver. Deposits of cholesterol, bile pigment and sometimes calcium in the gall-bladder may form gallstones. This is believed to result from the over-production of the cholesterol component.

Cholesterol is a substance necessary in the production of sex hormones in both male and female. This is one reason why gallstones are more common in women after pregnancy.

Bile is secreted by the liver and is stored in the gall-bladder before being released into the duodenum. The gallbladder extracts water from the bile within it and adds mucous, thus concentrating the bile. It is the perversion of this process in the sycotic individual that produces gallstones, gallstone colic, cholecystitis (inflammation) and obstructive jaundice, etc..

It is important to recognise the same ideas when differently expressed. The mucous secreted by the gallbladder, together with an over-production of cholesterol, when subjected to the process of crystallisation (grit) results in gallstones. Here is a perfect example of the sycotic process.

During metabolism excess cholesterol enters the bloodstream. Its over-production is stimulated by the over-indulgence in rich, fatty food, for which it is necessary to aid digestion. An excess of cholesterol in the bloodstream may lead to atheroslcerosis, and its consequences of embolism, thrombosis and ischaemia. The keynotes here again are over-production and the perversion of a natural chemical process. Heart and circulatory disease is not therefore merely the result of a high fat intake in the diet, though this is in itself undesirable for good health. Diet is only half the story, the other half being the perversion of the internal chemistry, having its origin in the sycotic miasm.

CHAPTER 13

CANCER

Cancer is the disease of our age, much as syphilis and tuberculosis were representative of the immediate centuries past. It has been observed how as tuberculosis declined, cancer increased to the same extent, until today cancer has become the most feared and probably the least understood disease of any. Sadly, cancer is the natural conclusion to our present state of being, it is the perfect reflection of the morbid and pathological processes existing in our society.

Cancer is a conclusion, a result of wrong endeavour, of twisted and suppressed emotions. It grows out of ignorance as to the proper handling of emotional power, that we are not educated to express correctly, but are taught to control and suppress. Emotional upheaval may quickly spread through a group, with fear and hysteria revealing itself with little provocation, such is the distress underlying our society. In addition, the horror of war is stamped upon the group mind of most nations, feeding a fear that will only decline slowly through the generations, unless a fresh contribution is made.

The amount of cancer that appears in a society is to some extent a comment on its values, and on us as the individuals who create and serve it. The refusal to admit that what happens in our lives is an expression of what is going on inside us, the one an exact reflection of the other, is a force serving the cause of cancer.

There are two ways of attaining the conclusion that is cancer, and they are both intimately bound up with each other: one is physical, the other emotional. For purposes of understanding, and homœopathic therapeutics, one of these areas is likely to be more apparent than the other in any individual, enabling the observer to gain an understanding of the processes involved. We shall plot the physical causes of cancer first, bearing in mind that the emotional will run concurrently, but may not be as intense or apparent a cause in an individual case.

The physical factors begin with inheritance; what the parents provide for the incarnating spirit. Or, to express it more truthfully, what the incarnating spirit brings with it. The parents fitting the child, and the child appropriate to the parents, "by their fruits shall you know them".

The next stage in the potential development of cancer occurs as the individual is exposed to modern medicine. Drug therapy, vaccinations and surgery will suppress disease expression so that very little is permitted to be eliminated from the individual, entombing disease as it were. We must bear in mind that the causes of disease are from within and not from without. The lack of awareness of this process is the cornerstone error of conventional therapeutic understanding.

We see the physical manifestation of cancer in the tumour or growth. Here the tendency to grow things – warts, polyps, fibroids, moles, veruccae, etc. – reaches its ultimate conclusion. All these growths belong together as an expression of the same disease process; known to homœopaths as the sycotic miasm. Though all three of the miasms of Hahnemann – psora, syphilis and sycosis – are present in the cancerous process, the sycotic contribution is the most easily observable

Those who can handle ideas should now be able to piece them together. The surgical removal of any growth whether cancerous or 'benign' does not cut out what produced it in the first place, but merely frustrates the expression of a disease which will, in due season, seek an alternative outlet. It is therefore unwise to remove warts, moles, polyps, fibroids and other growths at any time during the life unless they are pressing on a vital organ or threatening to block the air passages.

How can the development of cancer be most clearly charted? It is all too easy to observe how the accumulation of pus in the body forms an occult sepsis that then results in cancer. This is why antibiotics, so convenient in suppressing a septic state, are deadly to those depending on them. This is no flight of fancy. It is, fortunately, observable how cancer patients during homœopathic treatment have warts and moles returning as an accompaniment to greater health, and moreover how pussy discharges are the most reliable indication of a cancerous patient's progress towards cure.

Chapter 13

A cancerous tumour grows from within, and should therefore be cured from within, gently and permanently with natural therapeutics mobilising the hitherto perverted energies of the being to do their own work of restitution. The physical body possesses its own natural intelligence, even in the most desperate situations and should therefore be encouraged along its own path.

In short, the repeated manifestation of local septic states within the physical body, suppressed by antibiotics or surgery is the physical story of cancer. Repeated bouts of tonsilitis or quinsy in childhood will often result in excision of the offending glands. This severe suppression of a septic state is the beginning of a malignant path in which the body, frustrated in its attempts to rid itself of poisonous matter will putrify over the years. Even worse, and almost a specific for cancer in later years, is a so called mastoid infection. The area behind the ear becomes filled with pus, accompanied by fever and much pain. Usually the mastoid is cleared out and antibiotics employed, but the affliction often returns and the treatment repeated. The homœopathic remedy CARCINOSIN is nearly always indicated in such a case.

When taking detailed medical histories in cancer cases, local sepsis and the sycotic state have all too often played a key part in the drama. Those who reach homœopathic treatment before the malignant result most often do not get the cancer they were headed for. This is such worthwhile work even if the homœopath considers she has done little else for the patient.

In a larger context than that of the individual, cancer can be seen to be a consequence of a malignant society and its morbid components. Remember, that what is true on one level is also true on other levels. The physical tumour is composed of 'breakaway' cells that no longer serve the organ they comprise by the usual cooperation with their neighbours. They form their own smaller 'society' within the organ, no longer performing their duties towards the integrity of that organ. Such tumours may even develop their own skeletal and nervous systems. The result is a breakdown in organ function and integrity, leading to degeneration and death.

The analogue within society can be seen with the many breakaway groups prevalent today. These may be self-interested to the point of no longer serving the society within which they exist. The extreme example is the terrorist group prepared to destroy to get its own way.

The physical body and the higher vehicles of human expression work together to produce the peace and harmony of natural good health, rarely experienced by human beings today. A bodily organ works successfully by its component cells cooperating harmoniously. Weakness in one will in time put stress on others. The human body functions through the proper balance and working of its component organs. Society works by the cooperation of all its members.

We will now explore the emotional factors tending towards cancer. Mentally and emotionally cancer is a disease of morbidity; a morbid, chuntering, out of control brain that destroys the body. So many people feed their brains on morbid thoughts, frequently from newspapers and television programs, and then turn these thoughts over and over in a constant and habitual stirring of fearful emotions. It is a dark shadow that is drawn to the self by dwelling on morbid thoughts of terrible things it is feared will happen.

Morbidity enters in whenever we allow others to undermine our own authority and whenever we allow fear to rule instead of knowledge. Whenever you are manipulated through fear into taking action that you know to be incorrect, that is a morbid activity following a morbid thought process. The roots of fear have penetrated deep for any who believe that war will break out and imagine its consequences.

Cancer is a disease of fear, and primarily of anticipatory fear. People may be full of fear both in social and work situations. It is fear that paralyses action and impedes creativity. A fear of unworthiness and a lack of confidence will erode the creative life force, this will dam up energy and result in morbid disease.

Cancerous people are not using their potential, their creative energy becomes dammed up, with an attendant fear and chuntering on the mental and emotional level which results in morbidity on every level. Tuberculosis has its relationship with cancer because tubercular people are not expressing their energy through the physical body either. Tubercular people are disconnected from their physical bodies. They indulge in depression and morbid imaginings, using their dissatisfaction as an excuse to withdraw from the world. This disconnection leads to a state of perversion and disorganisation. The resulting chaos on this basic level makes it difficult to function creatively on any other.

With cancer the brain has become out of control, it follows its own habitual groove. When the morbid and unpleasant material of the petty self is constantly turned over, without direction from a higher and more creative influence, then it will cause the release of corrosive endocrine secretions into the body that will cause cancer. Very few people have any control over the habitual workings of the mind and so most people will experience this gramophone record type of thinking. With the cancerous person this brain activity has become an intense chuntering that continues day and night whenever the brain is not otherwise occupied. A danger sign is that they lay awake at night allowing a stream of morbid thoughts to run around their heads without following each thought through to its conclusion and then letting it go. Lying awake at night and chuntering is particularly destructive as things tend to seem worse than they really are then, and also the body should be resting so that the vitality can repair and regenerate it.

It serves a person well to gain some degree of control over the activity of the brain. Meditation can play a useful part in this process, as during meditation the brain is deliberately stilled.

CHAPTER 14

THE HEART CENTRE AND THE SYPHILITIC MIASM

The endocrine glands form a part of human anatomy as yet little understood by western medical science, but of such great importance and influence that future medical and judicial practice will be centered around the knowledge of them. The endocrine system is almost entirely responsible for the way we think, act and feel. As a result, many will, and some do now, consider themselves as helpless victims at the mercy of their glandular activity; this is not so.

The ductless glands secrete powerful chemicals into the bloodstream affecting the way we feel and behave. This is already partially understood in relation to the way women's hormones are observed to change behaviour patterns over the monthly cycle. However, this is a very small, if somewhat seized upon example of a much larger drama in which we are all involved.

The endocrine glands are working in various degrees of disharmony in the human race as presently constituted. It is this state of imbalance, unknown and unappreciated, which gives rise to so much illness, unhappiness and anti-social and criminal behaviour. These glands are influenced by what we do to ourselves, and are especially damaged by the injection of drugs (prescribed and otherwise) and innoculations.

The ductless glands and the sympathetic nervous system, of which they are a part, are the direct physical adjunct to the seven major centres of power in the human system, known as the chakras. These chakras are part of the vital body (vitality). Their development and unfoldment through right attitude and behaviour constitute no less than the vital route through which humanity must pass as it travels ever upwards on its evolutionary path. The role of the homœopathic prescriber here is of such great importance that exaggeration is impossible. Homœopathic remedies influence the health and balance of the chakras and their physical counterparts, the endocrine glands. It would therefore be of great advantage for homœopaths to become conscious of this process.

All life is energy vibrating at different rates. When the vibration slows sufficiently it becomes crystallised into matter; only then are we able to perceive it through our five physical senses. This applies equally to a human being as it does to the whole physical world around us. There is, therefore, no sharp dividing line between the spiritual and the material. It may help to bear this in mind when considering chakras, which most of us cannot see, and endocrine glands which being their physical counterpart it is possible to observe.

The activity of the chakras sets up a pattern within the human anatomy, influencing the endocrine glands to secrete chemicals into the bloodstream. This, in turn, affects our thoughts and behaviour, positively and negatively. The whole body, every cell and atom, must conform to this influence, forming a kind of pattern of agreement throughout the entire human organism. This is a two way process, and the chakras in their turn, must conform to the thoughts and feelings of the individual. Positive thoughts create healthy secretions, negative thoughts destructive secretions. The secretions influence the thoughts and feelings, creating a positive or negative cycle of habitual behaviour within each individual.

This is the compact disc which goes round in the brain forming a mental activity which, if persistantly negative, poisons the body to such a degree that chronic degenerative disease results. When the brain is idle, it will mull over old emotionally-charged activity (resulting from the endocrine glands). The way out of this loop is through an act of one's own will, by deliberately changing the brain's diet and output. Take a hold of the attitudes and change them where necessary from negative to positive. The fostering of goodwill towards others, kindly behaviour and a sunny outlook will do much to revolutionise the chakras and their endocrine output, thus directly changing the health of every cell within the being. Positive secretions encouraging a positive physical, emotional and mental manifestation, in turn enhance health and well-being.

What we think and feel is emanated into our atmosphere and, according to the law of 'like attracts like', will draw the same towards us. So when we feel and think the world is a wonder of God's creation, full of beauty and light, then we will draw experience of this quality towards us, thus confirming our feelings. Conscious and deliberate intervention on our own behalf, with persistant effort, constitutes Ariadne's thread out of the labyrinth of negativity. It is also a law that energy follows thought, creating the physical manifestion of whatever our idle and mischievous brains dwell upon.

The chakra system was expounded by the Hindus, Druids and others. It also constitutes the main body of Greek mythology. The chemical secretions were given the names of gods and goddesses, with their behaviour towards one another playing out the complex interaction of the centres and their glands. The Apocalypse recounts the story of one travelling through the churches in Asia (chakras) to become master of his own destiny. Medieval alchemists veiled their heretical knowledge of progressing up through the centres with tales of turning base lead (manifestation) into pure gold (seership).

Man's mental faculties are at present generally limited to the lower or concrete mind. It is here that he uses the reasoning powers of the intellect to guide and overcome his difficulties. What is limiting here is the arrogant assumption that the development of the intellect alone constitutes the totality of mental ability. There are other faculties yet to be won by humanity - through right behaviour, goodwill and concentration - and one of these is direct cognition, the ability to directly know something without the necessity of the intellectual process. Such knowledge is impressed upon the higher mind by contact with the spirit. This process is becoming manifest in more and more people today, although all too often what they say is dismissed as invalid, as the method cannot be proven.

The activation of the higher mind necessitates having an open heart centre. Love and compassion are the qualities required here, and learning to express these in our everyday life incubates the qualities at the heart centre. Compassion is the higher octave of sentimentality, a negative aspect of heart activity.

The heart is the seat of life and is the synthesis of the other centres of power. It is also called the sun centre, which radiates always without price. Here is found the Holy Grail of Arthurian legend. To the Chinese it is the Emperor, whose word is supreme. It is the Holy City, the Jerusalem of the Jews and Christians, the Mecca of the Muslims. Within all these traditions is stored knowledge of the great qualities and faculties of the heart.

The right secretion at the heart centre gives a nature which is honourable in all things, noble and aspiring. It gives stability and power, steadfast unswerving action, and great self control. A positive heart centre is about being open and honest in all things. The alternative secretion produces the arrogant, domineering person - the tyrant and despot - or the impulsive, rash person easily led by their feelings, which leads to different forms of dissipation. They suffer from defective heart action and poor circulation. They are also likely to develop feverish complaints that react on the mind, bringing gloom, despair, discord and lack of concentration.

The heart centre is the fourth centre up the spine, a point of change. It is said that when this centre is developed, man will enter fully into the human kingdom, his animal side having been overcome. He becomes his own authority, not relying upon the spoken word of another, but making his own judgements for himself.

There are several homœopathic remedies which principally affect the heart centre, the main one of which is NATRUM MUR. Some others are SYPHILINUM, TUBERCULINUM and AURUM.

NATRUM MUR, with its suppressed emotion, hidden motives, lack of openess and honesty, provides a fine picture of blocked heart activity. The feelings of sentimentality, grief, depression, desire to spurn human company, and anger give a remedy picture of a heart struggling with itself. Its symptom complex is well known and documented by many prescribers and teachers, it is therefore not necessary to illustrate it fully here. Anyone blocked in this area will need NATRUM MUR in high potency. IGNATIA will also be required, and may be used in low potency to run concurrently, as a drainage remedy for the heart and lungs.

The heart centre and the thymus gland directly affect the organs within the chest, namely the physical heart and lungs, and also the arms and hands. The sense of smell is also associated with it.

At this point of evolution humanity stands at a vast crossroads. We are rapidly concluding both a century and a millenium. We are also entering the next great cycle of two thousand or so years, known as the Age of Aquarius, and it is during this coming period that humanity's sensitivities of clairvoyance and psychic abilities are to be awakened. It is the age when true religion will be cultivated in the daily life and not just on Sunday mornings. Man will come to realise his true nature, and much of what we value now as knowledge will become the focus of some considerable amusement. Great theories will be torn down and human idols defrocked as truths come tumbling forth.

To facilitate this process, the heart centre is being opened up by those guides and guardians of the human race who work tirelessly for its eventual triumph, in much the same way as the good groundsman guides the activity of his charges to cultivate growth and beauty in the garden. The mother is an important link in healing the heart centre. In general, the heart centre is more blocked in males than in females, and women tend to be more in touch with their feelings and more expressive of them than men.

The opening of the heart centre on a mass scale began with the great wars between 1914 and 1945, for at this time the outpouring of great anger, violence and revenge became inevitable. It was necessary to sweep away all the old orders and values, and if the young generation that followed had not rebelled against their elders, it would have seen the end of humanity.

The worst observable block to the heart centre today comes from innoculation. It can be said that innoculation is similar to venereal disease in that it creates a miasmatic condition within the individual. In fact it is worse, more elusive and more difficult to treat than venereal disease. Without the gross violation of immunisation, our receptivity, sensitivity, knowledge, memory, concentration, self discipline and spiritual contact would all be much better. Innoculation is the grossest malpractice and perpetrator of illusion in our age. Sometimes the soul cannot fulfill its destiny as a result and must return home (death); herein lies the reason for many cot deaths. Cot death was unknown prior to innoculation

Innoculation gives rise to sexual perversion, a problem which will become worse the more we persist in immunising our children, especially among males. This is particularly true of the innoculation against mumps (part of the MMR vaccine). So we have created problems of sexuality, childish behaviour, unexpressed feelings, disease, unrest and disharmony on all levels. The innoculated individual is never at peace, they are a restless soul searching here and there for something which can only be found within. Innoculation is the main reason today why the heart centre cannot radiate love, and humanity is maintained in a state of conflict, self-interest and dissatisfaction.

The havoc caused by innoculation affects all the endocrine glands. The glandular secretions in the immunised individual become perverse. Cells in the brain become active when they should not and all manner of perverted feelings and thoughts become unleashed. The immune system may be confused for ever. The spirit does not sit properly in the body.

The immune and endocrine systems meet at the thymus gland, where they form the hub of the human mandala. The immune system and the endocrine system must be in balance to produce good health. It is said that the thymus gland contains many T-lymphocytes, those cells largely responsible for a healthy immune system. These lymphocytes, and the immune system in general, are destroyed by innoculation, antibiotics and other substances from modern drug therapy. Innoculation produces and encourages 'bad soldiers', who open the doors to allow disease into the system. It is a great source of cancer, a mix of all the miasms. Smoking, alcohol and polluted atmospheres also weaken the etheric web and promote disease.

The gross malfunction resulting from innoculation causes

criminal behaviour, anger and wars that are unnecessary for humanity to experience. There are those negative and self-interested forces who, having seen the New Age coming, have blocked the heart centre deliberately, thus preventing enlightenment. A veil of lies has been drawn over the history of innoculation, while it has been aggressively marketed.

There is rarely any specific antidote to innoculation, though this may be achieved to some degree if homœopathic treatment is administered very soon after. Normally, a potency of the innoculation - for example DPT 30, or MMR 30 - repeated over a few days will work. However, the blight soon penetrates the whole being, physical, emotional, mental and spiritual, so that the concept of 'antidote' may no longer be a framework for consideration.

Using the indicated homœopathic remedies, constitutional or otherwise, will gradually repair innoculation damage. However, sometimes the damage to the immune system is so great that it will never be completely restored. Often the biochemic cell salt corresponding to the patient's sun sign, plus the rising-sign cell salt (for those of you who appreciate astrology), given alternately over a long period will be of assistance in reducing innoculation damage. The use of THYMUS GLAND 6x, also given over a long period of time, and a dose of NATRUM MUR in high potency, will be helpful for those individuals who have had their heart centres destroyed by innoculation.

The Thymus Gland

The thymus gland is the ductless gland situated in the chest. It lies in front of the upper part of the heart and the great vessels in the chest, immediately behind the upper portion of the breast bone. It is a large structure composed of a cortex of cells resembling lymphocytes, and an inner portion in which round clusters of flattened cells are found.

The thymus grows rapidly in the child until the second year, then more slowly, and at the age of puberty it begins to regress. In adult life its presence is shown only by rudiments.

It is claimed that the thymus lost much of its value for man and mammals when their ancestors began to incubate their eggs within their body and ceased laying them, as do birds and reptiles. The original function of the thymus was in the production of albumen and shells. Pigeons whose thymus has been removed lay eggs without shells, but if fed thymus extract, will lay normal eggs with shells. We must be grateful for the thymus, because its secretions made it possible for our reptilian ancestors to invent an egg that could evolve into a human ovum.

The thymus has been called the gland of precocity. It has also been named the gland of eternal youth, for its failure to retrogress at the proper time inhibits the maturing of the body. When thymus is fed to a tadpole, it remains a tadpole and does not metamorphose into a frog. In a book by Williams and Hoag, entitled "Our Fear Complexes", it is stated that out of twenty executed criminals, "all had persistent thymus glands".

If the thymus is over-active, it has a tendency to prevent the normal differentiation of sex expression, resulting in 'intermediate' types. The large increase of this equation in our social system warrants profound consideration of the part played by the ductless glands in the social life of man.

In the past it was believed that at puberty the thymus atrophied but it is now known that some of its secreting cells remain active throughout life. When too many of these cells persist, the gland becomes from five to ten times as large as normal, and a number of other features become prominent which make the individual extra-ordinary. It is the gland that keeps children childish, and sometimes makes children out of adults.

During childhood the thymus is the organ that promotes the growth of bones, but at puberty a decreased functioning begins. It is believed that the sex glands arising to a functional level at that time, exert a restraining influence upon it. With its role in egg-shell formation in birds and reptiles, and bone formation in mammals, the assimilation and distribution of lime throughout the human economy appears to be influenced by the thymus gland. Is this the physiology behind the CALCAREA symptom picture?

The secretion of the thymus is called thymovidin and is believed to be the controller of the growth of children. When an enlarged thymus is present in a newborn baby, the breathing reflex may be delayed, and such a baby is said to be born blue. If a child is under-nourished there is a rapid decline in the weight of the gland, so the state of a child's thymus is an indication of the condition of the body.

The secretions of the thymus gland also control muscular metabolism during the period of childhood. It also influences the development of the adrenal cortex, the pineal gland, the thyroid gland, and the prostate gland. So from the heart centre its influence radiates upwards and downwards. Children nursed on human milk have greater vitality than those brought up on the milk of animals, because animal ether is not permanently absorbed by the thymus gland as human ether is.

The thymus gland is the reception centre for psychic information. However, our thymus function has been severely blocked by the syphilitic and tubercular miasms, and most of all by innoculation. The centre at the base of the spine is also seriously damaged by innoculation; faculties at this centre concern organisation, memory and the ability to do things as and when they need doing. Diseases from negative base centre activity include tuberculosis, gallstones and kidney stones.

It is known that the removal of the thymus gland does not result in death. Likewise, the removal of the spleen does not result in death. However, the removal of the thymus gland and the spleen does result in death. As the thymus gland governs the growth of bones in the child, what implications are there for the blood-making marrow? The increasing incidence of leukaemia could well be partly a result of the damage done to the thymus gland in young people by innoculation.

We have illustrated the importance of the thymus gland to the development of the child and the sexual function. We have also described how the thymus gland is at the hub of the immune system. The result of mass innoculation programs is that the thymus gland in most people has been so damaged that their whole endocrine systems' have been put out of balance. These are the conditions that we now have to deal with. Homœopathic prescribers must urge the prevention of innoculation wherever possible. This cannot be pursued too strongly, even if it means that patients fail to return; they must be given an opportunity to hear what is said.

Chapter 14

The Heart Centre and Syphilis

We live as part of the fifth great Root Race of human evolution. Each Root Race lasts some millions of years. This current Aryan epoch is a time when the faculty of mind is being developed. We have to think, even if just a little, in order to maintain a reasonable standard of life. At the same time, we are cut off, it seems, from any conscious contact with higher spiritual life; so much so that men pour scorn on the very idea.

The last great Root Race was that of Atlantis, of which most of us living now were a part. At that time physical bodies were less dense, and humanity had an almost continuous dialogue with beings on other planes of consciousness. All the stories of gods, heroes and men, fairy tales, wicked witches and other fantastic legends come from this age, and bear its truth upon their wings. Merlin is a quality handed down to us from the Atlantean epoch. Man lived more comfortably within himself and the hub of his existence, the heart, was understood to be the Garden of Eden.

At the time of Atlantis man was developing his heart centre, the fourth stage up the spine, and the faculty of desire. Magic was much practised in Atlantis and did not have the evil stigma now awarded to it. However, the cardinal sin of the Atlanteans became theft, driven by desire. Desire took a foothold as they did not have the constraining faculty of mind, which we are hopefully developing. Magic was eventually used for personal desire and gain, and thus became black magic. So great became the desire, that man's consciousness was driven out of his body and he became aware, almost exclusively, of the world outside himself and his desire to possess everything he saw. The heart was blackened and the result was war - the first half of the war that was later played out again in our present Century. The first time, the forces of good were not successful and Atlantis was destroyed, and purified by water by sinking beneath the waves. The spirit of the earth had intervened in the conflict.

The remnants of this great Age travelled to Tibet, Egypt, South America and Britain, to set up new schools of development.

The consequence of all this is that man was driven downwards, or more accurately, outwards from his state of harmony.

Consciousness is now outside himself, and within is the syphilitic miasm. Man therefore has syphilitic karma because he destroyed himself in Atlantis.

All the heavy karma we have experienced over the period we call history up to the present time comes from Atlantis. But now, especially after the horrors of the Great War of this Century, we have a chance of regeneration. At this time of the dawning of a New Age, once again man stands at the gate of his heart, ready to receive enlightenment. Hopefully, this time the restraining faculty of mind will be sufficiently developed to afford success. Though materialism has reached some nauseating levels in some parts of the world, it has only once reached the depraved desires of Atlantis.

Anyone today who is at all tainted by the syphilitic miasm is Atlantean. All our trials and struggles in this life and the lessons we learn, are dedicated to regaining our lost ascendency. This is why it is now so important that the heart centre and the thymus gland be cleared of its blocks. As may be deduced from the story of Atlantis, the thymus centre is not only a psychic reception area for good, but also for evil. Here we stand upon the podium of true humanity - there is always choice and the freedom to choose - it is up to us.

All the seeds of desire sown in Atlantis must be worked out in the realm of form (this life). It is from the Desire Body that most of our disease originates. How we use what we receive from the Desire Body through the heart centre will determine our future progress. If we employ this knowledge in the service of others, for the selfless good of all humanity, then ours will be a just reward. If we use it for selfish desire then we will begin to repeat the mistakes of the past, "And I will give to all his rightful share" the saying goes. The Bible is as yet unveiled by most.

It is at the heart centre that we become true humanity, responsible for ourselves in the full light of knowledge. Let us make a beginning.

As the heart centre is opened, it is said that the mystic seeks the 'Bride of the Lord'. This is veiled language for liberating the qualities of this chakra, namely the faculty of direct knowing, the radiation of love and compassion, together with the opening of the thymus gland as a psychic centre of reception. The religionist fails to recognise her, though he embraces her in his arms.

From the heart centre a darker side or a false psychism can be generated. In the Apocalypse it is depicted as the pseudo-seeress, Jezebel. She represents the emotional, erotic expression of psychism which may be developed at orgiastic religious revivals. It is a prostitution of the mind and emotions to the base or animal nature, causing moral disintegration and the dissipation of psychic energy. Mediumistic faculties may sometimes be developed opening up avenues of communication with the discarnate, to whom the misguided medium offers as food aspects of his own degenerating self.

The mythical character of Ixion coveted Hera, the wife of Zeus (presider over the generative centre). Knowing this, Zeus sent Ixion a cloud in the form of Hera, upon whom Ixion begat Centaurus. The story is one of rampant desire and acquisition. For this attempt on Hera, Ixion was chained to a perpetually rolling wheel by Hermes (presider over the brow centre).

This wheel represents the cycle of rebirth and Ixion represents humanity. It was in Atlantis that man first consciously learned of and experienced death as a result of his evil activity at that time. Man no longer realised he was immortal, the memory of what occurred between the tomb and the womb had gone. Man had inherited syphilitic and tuberculous karma, diseases that grew up inside him and killed him. It is interesting to note that Ixion was chained to his wheel by Hermes. Hermes represents mind, the faculty now being developed in order, we hope, to control and direct desire. Also, Zeus begat Hermes on Maya, where Maya represents illusion, the world of form.

The frantic, violent, hyperactive and out of control behaviour of many of our children is an illustration - caused and influenced by innoculation - of the terrible unhappiness and evil of not only consciousness being outside ourselves, but of being totally outside ourselves, with even less chance of regaining rightful access. The soul is shut out from its vehicles.

The Centaurs, half man and half beast, are depicted as mostly badly behaved and antisocial. They represent man in the grip of animal desire. Now that consciousness and desire have become externalised, they must be worked out in the world of form. Not all the Centaurs remained this way; some such as Chiron received wisdom and therefore showed themselves capable of regeneration.

Syphilinum and Tuberculinum

Syphilis represents the essence of all that is most evil and dark that humanity has vested upon itself. It is negativity incarnate, and evil forces feed upon its manifestation. Syphilis hides in its own darkness, weaving its tentacles like a hydra within a disintegrating personality. It hides and mutates and may look like the other miasms.

Syphilis has its seat in the heart and from there perpetrates its evil shadows. It often looks like NATRUM MUR - the principle remedy of the heart centre. Most heart disease is syphilitic in origin. Many times good prescribers have failed in an obvious NATRUM MUR picture where the remedy did not work or only temporarily relieved the patient; then SYPHILINUM would have worked.

Doubt and illusion - doubt in one's self and one's abilities, self-hate, self-deprivation, low self-esteem, guilt, unworthiness, an attraction to accidents, disasters and horrific afflictions, violence, rape, suicidal depression - all form the substance of the syphilitic miasm.

As we know, active syphilis may remain hidden with the sufferer exhibiting few symptoms, if any, for several years. Then perhaps a chancre appears which heals or may pass unnoticed. In time madness descends upon its host, which in the third and final stage of the disease becomes an insanity which destroys coherence and undermines the ability to function to a reasonable standard. However, if a keen observer looks at the history, it can be seen how the disease has shaped the destruction of the individual from its inception. As a miasm, syphilis is also hidden and may masquerade as almost anything, it may appear nothing like its scant review in the materia medicas.

We are masters of illusion in this age - the advertisers can make anything look what it is not. Food manufacturers create any taste in a laboratory. And as we survey the patient, we may wonder if it is one remedy or another as the syphilitic miasm wafts through our consciousness. Much of what we hold to be true and demonstrable is in fact an illusion.

There will be a darkness and a fear trying to remain unnoticed within the syphilitic person. There will be a shadow of negativity creeping like something out of a Kafka novel throughout their life. Then, suddenly, something will awaken the slumbering monster from the dark recesses of the being. A living hell will be unleashed upon the person; something that has never been experienced before.

The well known syphilitic symptoms of boils, abscesses, sleeplessness, depression and obsessions may or may not be present. During its hidden phase its presence may be marked only by the subtle forces of destruction working in the life of the patient. There may be a dread that the patient may be aware of, or may be so taken for granted as to be assumed 'natural'. The dread is an awareness of what lies in the dark recesses of the being, of what terrible events wait around the corner trying to remain unnoticed. There may be an unusual fascination or fear of the macabre. It is the suddenness and seeming cruelty with which things happen that will make the grip of the miasm evident to all.

The eruption of the syphilitic miasm into the life may be triggered off by a shock, accident, illness or the taking of drugs (prescribed or otherwise). It is not unusual for the birth control pill to act as a major precurser to this miasm. Like the other venereal diseases, syphilis originates in the generative organs as a result of the abuse of the qualities of this area. The pill suppresses the natural function at the heart of female power - the ovaries - and thus unleashes its dark side, or shadow.

The keen observer may recognise the forces of the syphilitic miasm at work before they unleash chaos and destruction in the life of the patient. It is better when treating a patient in the grip of the syphilitic miasm to prescribe the remedy SYPHILINUM in medium potencies - the 30th centisimal for example - over a long period of time. High potencies of the nosode will tend to pass straight through, which may benefit an ancestor of the patient, but not the patient themself. It may also be judicious to use drainage remedies in low potency, directed at the appropriate organ or area of the body. Use the other indicated or constitutional remedies also, and in so doing help weave the rich tapestry of the patient's evolution.

The tubercular miasm is the least hidden of all the miasms. It is usually quite plain to see, and of all this group of disease remedies it probably has the best picture in materia medicas. Like syphilinum, tuberculinum too is much centered on the heart, often concealing a syphilitic taint. If you can't treat syphilitics one way, you probably can this way. The tubercular miasm contains all the miasms, so TUBERCULINUM is often followed well with the sycotic nosode, MEDORRHINUM, or equally by SYPHILINUM.

Tuberculosis has over the decades mutated into cancer. Tubercular patients tend also to be cancerous and may require a dose of the remedy CARCINOSIN, as do their children. The administration of these remedies gently steers them away from the possibility of producing cancer. Prescribing the remedy CARCINOSIN will often bring to the surface the main or principle miasm if in doubt.

The tubercular miasm tends towards perversity in its manifestation. It is often a useful remedy in cases of violence, particularly domestic violence, rape, incest and other forms of sexual abuse. Sexual perversions and crimes require remedies that act on the sexual sphere, and those remedies which affect this area of the body and the glands involved. Here we see the syphilitic side of the tubercular miasm.

Tubercular patients are perverse, and their acutes are sudden, obscure, painful, and often difficult to treat. They are the people who will take lots of remedies between visits to the homœopath, thus obscuring the case. They are nervous and highly strung to the extreme, often frantic, and it is with tubercular people that we see so obviously portrayed the restless searching outside themselves for a satisfaction which always remains elusive, driving the person ever onwards.

The sycotic side of the tubercular miasm comes out in rheumatism, arthritis, iritis, asthma, hayfever, etc., together with the acute diseases of the upper air passages, suffered by so many of our children. A mixture of the tubercular miasm, sycosis and innoculation is responsible for this and these disorders can normally be removed entirely by homœopathic treatment.

Sometimes TUBERCULINUM fails to benefit an obvious tuberculous case. CALCAREA CARB will often take up and complete the work here. Also consider the nosode SYPHILINUM.

APPENDIX

ANATOMY AND PHYSIOLOGY

Introduction to Appendix

The following section has largely been based on a book called the "Rosicrucian Cosmo-Conception", written by Max Heindel, and published by the Rosicrucian Fellowship who have kindly given permission to use the material. Much of the language has been changed to enable the introduction of material relevant to homœopathy.

There is much talk about the Vital Force in homœopathy, but who really understands what this means? Similarly, who really understands how the mind, emotions and physical body interact? Or how we are a truly spiritual integrity? The "Rosicrucian Cosmo-Conception" offers the best explanation that I know of these questions, and the author feels it necessary that students and practitioners of homœopathy should begin to appreciate and understand this information.

A knowledge of these systems, combined with an understanding of the chakra/endocrine system, will enable the practitioner to begin to comprehend the various complex levels upon which a human being functions both as an individual and on a group level. I would strongly encourage us all to learn to identify the various parts of our occult anatomy and physiology, thereby bringing to the forefront of personal experience the spiritual integrity and beauty of each human being and thus enabling a greater understanding of the homœopathic work.

Appendix

ANATOMY AND PHYSIOLOGY

We are each a spark of divine light descended into matter shaped by form, and striving for conscious ascendancy through the organisation of the material world. Man is a unity, a myriad complexity of impulse, expression, thought and occasionally manifestation of spirit, striving to be at one with himself and his natural environment, as the highest expression of and the material instrument of nature. Man is body, mind and spirit.

THE PHYSICAL WORLD

That which we generally refer to as the body is composed of two parts – the physical, or chemical, and vital, the seat of 'vital force'. The body has seven sub-divisions. Three of these sub-divisions we relate to in the physical world – solids, liquids and gases; while the other four belong to the vital body and are called ethers. It is the three former divisions that society and material science relate to exclusively, giving no credence to the existence of any other world or vehicle of expression. It is in this world of solids, liquids and gases that the end results of activities in the other worlds may be observed, e.g. in the human organism by the manifestation of disease. As the chemical world is regarded by orthodoxy as all that exists, they see only effect and construct new elaborate 'scientific' theories to explain physical phenomena which cannot be otherwise understood under such poverty of vision. In this way cause and effect are confused. What is called cause is only effect at a stage deeper. In the study of disease the further back we can trace cause the greater is our understanding.

The chemical or physical body is the medium through which

the vital vehicle manifests. The chemical body is dead matter and is only given life as it is created in the matrix of the vital body by the quickening spirit in the womb. The unity of these vehicles remains throughout the incarnation, the spirit seeking an ever closer contact with them, in order to fulfil its purpose. It is the vital body which gives life and animation to the chemical. It is engaged in a constant battle to repair and rebuild the damage done through the act of living and becoming older. Without it life would not be possible. At death it leaves the chemical vehicle which reverts to dead matter. The chemical vehicle is of the world and is cast off by the spirit like an old overcoat at the end of the incarnation. The purely chemical activities take over and a process of decomposition sets in as nature completes the great alchemical drama.

As stated, the vital body consists of four sub-divisions or ethers. The positive and negative forces of assimilation and excretion work through the chemical ether. The assimilation and distribution of food and nutrients through the positive pole build and maintain the physical vehicle. Any diseases of food allergy or mal-assimilation will show some disorder in the chemical ether.

Excretion is carried out through the negative pole of the chemical ether. Excretion includes the expulsion of all non-assimilative material and that which has outlived its use in the body; mucous, pus, catarrh, lymphatic congestion, etc.. These are potentially disease producing substances indicating the body's need to excrete efficiently. They can accumulate at a faster rate than an excretory system can deal with them, and for example those who do not sweat, are constipated or show signs of some urinary difficulty have signs of dysfunction in this vehicle. Negative pole activity does not mean inferior. All these processes are necessary.

Life ether is the vehicle through which the forces concerned with the maintenance and continuation of the species operate; the organs of generation and their potency. It too has a positive and negative polarity.

Light ether has different activity in different grades of form. In the higher animals and man, it is responsible for generating that blood heat which makes them individually warm blooded.

This is positive pole activity. The negative pole manifests the non-active functions of sight, hearing, feeling, tasting and smelling. It also builds and maintains the eye. In cold-blooded animals the positive and negative poles are reversed.

Reflecting ether is also known as the great scribe or recorder. Everything that has ever happened to the being leaves a meticulous duplicate upon this vehicle. All actions, thoughts, impulses, and ideas create an impression upon the reflecting ether. It is the reflective memory of nature, though real memory is less diffused and is the quality of a higher realm. It is here that our activity is registered and reflected back to us as habit, both good and bad. Any activity, whether physical, emotional or mental, continuously indulged in creates an impression on the reflecting ether, creating the passive phenomena of repetition without thought. It does not discriminate between good or bad, it just is. Conscious updating of habitual mental activity, together with ruthless weeding out of old unworthy habits is required in order to move on in a balanced and even manner. Failure to do this is the cause of much pain and disruption in life. As everything in life happens in sequence, at any given stage some areas may be up to date while others are not, creating imbalance and difficulty. Reflecting ether is also the medium through which thought makes an impression on the physical brain.

Here a wider understanding and a different point of view should now be emerging from the reader. We have on the physical plane become fairly well organised as science attempts to explain the chemical realm in terms of itself. While we pay homage to the dwarfs of the scientific world, where are the men and women of vision? We are all creatures of action; whether that activity has direction or not it is up to us. We can use forethought or leave it to karma.

As the physical body is created in the matrix of the vital vehicle, it is an exact replica of the latter, with one exception. Man has a negative vital body and woman a positive one. The power of a woman's vital body generates more blood than she needs. It is important for a woman to express her emotions because in this instance the emotions act as a safety valve, without which the integrity of the physical casing is threatened. The monthly flow releases this pressure, which is why if the menses are suppressed there is great disruption on the emotional level. This explains why women are more readily and easily vitalised than men, their stamina often greater than that of man's and in many cases they are able to recover and continue longer than men. A healthily menstruating woman is renewed after each monthly flow.

The relation between vitality and blood generation gives the connection between the contraceptive pill and heart disease. Most women who take the pill suffer a reduction in vitality, some to such a degree that they have no aura at all, and are not possible to treat homœopathically. The vital body forms part of what is called the aura or energy field which surrounds all human beings, animals and plants. Minerals have energy but it is not individual, being instead planetary. The aura is felt and perceived by many and seen by some. Through it we project all our thoughts, feelings and impulses out into the world, drawing back to us substance of the same nature under the law of like attracts like. Therefore, if you believe the world to be a dangerous place then that is what it will be for you. If you believe people are kind and helpful then that is what they will be.The aura is read by psychics and may be changed by the individual through right thought and action, and goodwill.

Contained within the aura are the seven centres of power, called the chakras. Their more chemical adjuncts are the endocrine glands and sympathetic nervous system. These centres govern personality as we know it. They function to varying degrees and combinations in each individual and have a higher and lower expression – played out in our lives. It is the enriching and ennobling of thought, emotion and action which develops these centres and the individual on the spiritual quest of liberation from physical bondage, and they are profoundly influenced by homœopathy. If this is done consciously by both giver and receiver then the result will be enduring. Since we are subject to our glands of personality, it would do well to be consciously so.

The centres and their glands are also greatly affected by sound. It was necessary after the Second World War for incoming spirits to receive new information (which they did not) and turn humanity in a different direction with fresh activity. This can be seen in the steady growth of alternative culture (including homœopathy), which gains influence with each generation and is presently beginning to impinge on the pillars of establishment. However, the incoming spirits were not properly prepared and despite the right impulse, the centres of personality were encrusted in old habits, preventing the purpose from unfolding. The driving power of rock music was used as the vehicle of rebellious youth to stir up the endocrine glands and allow change to occur.

In ill health it is the vital body which is disordered, the effects of which may be observed in the physical vehicle. In health it radiates; what is then observed is happiness, joy and abundant energy. The difference between the two may be only a thought or an attitude! Radiant health is the natural inheritance of all humanity, while we bring forth disease, vaccination and drugs to destroy it. It is so foreign to humanity in its present state that on the rare occasions it is observed, is often mistaken for a spiritual state.

This is the area where homœopathic remedies are said to act, directly on the vital vehicle. They stimulate the vitality to do its own work of reorganisation and repair. The physical vehicle conforms to that of the vital vehicle. If change takes place on any of the inner planes and is maintained long enough, the others must conform. Within an instant of taking a homœopathic remedy its quality is registered in the vital body, it then settles between the nervous system and the circulation in the physical body and enters the meridians of energy. These meridians may be likened to water, in its liquid form these lines cannot be ordinarily observed, however, when ice forms, lines may be easily seen amidst its solid structure. The wondrous pattern of a snowflake is somewhat similar.

The physical world to which we relate is considered by material science to be the only realm of existence. However, we know this is not so, and in acknowledging this we realise that this physical plane is the realm of effect, whilst cause is something which happens elsewhere. It is of great importance for physicians and healers to learn about the other worlds, for we cannot heal by working with the physical world, the world of effect only. Material medicine confuses cause and effect, always attempting to find cause in the realm of effect only. Whatever they may say is cause, is in fact only effect, the cause of which lies in a chain of unseen events, having its origin elsewhere. We can to a certain extent realise these events by plotting the course of physical effects through someone's life by meticulous attention to aetiology.

But how do we know of these other vehicles of human expression? We have no proof, but if we look the evidence is overwhelming. We relate to the physical world through the five senses, without these we would not know the physical world existed. We know what electricity can do but we cannot see it. We see only its physical evidence. Equally, there lies latent within all human beings the ability to acquire first-hand knowledge of these worlds and those who populate them. However, few are willing to lead the life necessary or generate the discipline and persistence of effort required. For these qualities are vital if any advance on this path is to be achieved. It requires a certain development of the self, a knowledge of self, a humility of realisation of the truth of oneself. "If you will give a little, they will give a lot". If you will give but five minutes a day, the Gods will have to increase either your time or your capacity.

As stated, life is a hierarchy; the advance of the one at the top depends on the movement of the one at the bottom. There is no individual salvation. Hence the Egyptians illustrated the hierarchy of life as a pyramid.

In this New Age, the emphasis is on knowledge and our individual and collective capacity to know through experience. The previous two thousand or so years concentrated on belief and the spreading of such through fire and sword. Belief is no longer enough, but note the confusion made between the two – belief and knowledge – by those in public life.

THE DESIRE WORLD

With the physical and vital vehicles together we have a being capable of movement and physical maintenance and regeneration, but no reason for doing so. The desire world is the realm of emotion, of passions and desires on a lower level, and also of aspiration and altruism on a higher. This is the power house, our reason for doing, our incentive for action. It permeates every atom of the vitalised body urging it to move us this way or that. Without it there would be no experience or knowledge. While the law of the physical world is inertia, the desire world is in a state of unceasing motion. It is not therefore just finer physical matter. The desire world is a scintillating riot of colour, an ever-changing myriad of subtle shades of light and hue, where the forces of animal and man intermingle with innumerable hierarchies of spiritual beings who are as active there as we are here.

As in the physical world, there are seven sub-divisions. However, the material of desire stuff does not differ in nature as it does in the physical world, and permeates the desire world as material for the embodiment of desire.

This world of feeling, desire and emotion is under the dominance of two great powers – the forces of attraction and repulsion. In the three finer regions of the desire world the force of attraction alone holds sway, while repulsion is the dominant factor in the three lower regions, although attraction also has influence here. The central region is neutral, and is the region of feeling. It is here that the fate of an idea or impulse is decided by interest or indifference, bringing into play the two great forces, thereby relegating them to one region or another, or expelling them altogether.

It is the nature of all forms in the desire world to attract to them others of a like nature and to manifest in the physical world. In the lowest region of the desire world the forces of repulsion are at their strongest, and the forms here are forced apart with some considerable conviction, for it is in this region that the forms are created by the coarsest of passions and desires generated by man and beast. If the force of attraction was to dominate the lower regions, the accumulation and manifestation of evil would spread chaos throughout the universe. Thus man is afforded a certain amount of protection as in the field of evolution he is like a child with a lot of growing up to do.

Everything that happens in the physical world is reflected in all the other realms of nature, building its own form in each. In the desire world is built all that happens, all that is hoped would happen and all that is feared might happen. When a true account is related of an occurrence, another form is created like the first and these two are mutually attracted, giving strength to the other by virtue of their unity. If an untrue account is given a different and antagonistic form is created. They are attracted to each other as they deal with the same occurrence, but when their vibrations differ they act upon each other with mutual destruction.

This conflict between the facts and the differing versions of the facts have repercussions in all realms, not least the physical where much unhappiness and disruption can occur in life through lies and deceit. Evil, conscious excuses, malicious lies and deliberate deviousness will kill off anything that is good if indulged in for long enough. Repetition strengthens the destructive forms thus created.

The popular anachronism, to kill off desire, is not the answer, but mastery of the myriad powers of earth the preferred route, with emancipation instead of escape the recognised goal. Withdrawal from life is not the path to experience, or its fruit – first-hand knowledge. Non-participation is a lost opportunity based on fear and indifference excused by intellectualism. Mastery of the art of living is the way to fulfilment. We need to learn how to act, to feel and to think then manifest right action, right feeling and right thought.

It should be realised by now that through the original impulse to be here, we have no choice. The choice we have is how to be. The nature of the atmosphere we create about ourselves is dependent on the feelings we generate. At any instant we breathe into our lungs every thought and feeling we create, via the aura. From the lungs it is impressed on the blood, and we wonder why there is so much disease and disorder.

Seeking the good amidst evil will in time transmute the evil into good. Again, if the form is strong and repeated often enough it will destroy the evil form and replace it with the good. Therefore looking for the good in all things has the effect of keeping down the evil. This is often expressed in folklore, but now it should be possible to gain a glimpse of the mechanics involved in this process.

The second sub-division of the desire world is the region of impressionability and here the forces of attraction and repulsion are evenly balanced, forming a neutral area. The feeling is neutral and separate from any feeling engendered by the fourth region. Here pictures are formed by the forces of sense perception in the vital body of man.

In the third region the force of attraction – the integrating upbuilding force – is gaining greater influence over the force of repulsion or disintegration. The mainspring of this force of repulsion is self-assertion, a pushing away of all others in order to have space; it gives way most easily to a desire for other things, so that the substance of the third region of the desire world is dominated by the force of attraction towards other things, but in a selfish way. It is therefore known as the region of wishes.

The first region of the desire world, that of coarse desire, has its synonym in the solids of the physical world, the region of impressionability to the fluids, and the ever-changing area of the region of wishes to the gaseous area of the physical world.

These three regions of the desire world give the substance for the forms which make for experience, soul growth and evolution, purging that which is entirely destructive and retaining the materials which may be used for progress.

The fourth region of the desire world is that of feeling. From it come the feelings concerning the forms and the life they have, for it is dependent upon the feelings engendered by them; also the effect they have on us. It is not important here whether the emotions are good or bad, it is the nature of our feelings, whether interest or indifference, that determines the fate of the object or idea. Here, interest gives life to a thing, feeds it, makes it grow. Indifference starves it, makes it die.

From this region of the desire world emanate the incentives to refrain from desire as a means of escape from the responsibilities of life and the work engendered thereby.

For interest awakens the forces of attraction and repulsion and from the ensuing struggle comes all the pain and suffering incident to wrong doing, or misdirected effort, whether intentional or otherwise. Indifference will wither the matter away, the result; inaction or non-participation in life. Much of this has its root in pride, "why should I?", so because we can't have our own way and dictate the rules we, "take our ball home and refuse to play". The feelings we have determine the nature of the atmosphere we create for ourselves and therefore the world as we experience it.

The three upper regions of the desire world are: the region of soul-life, the region of soul-light, and the region of soul-power. In these abide art, altruism and philanthropy, pure aspiration, the desire to serve, and all the activities of the higher soul life. These three regions have the capacity to radiate the qualities indicated by their names into the forms of the three lower regions, thus refining and uplifting the being.

It is in the desire world that most disease has its origins. The passions and coarse desires of the lower animal realms are the most powerful, as they were developed and worked upon first through the four kingdoms of nature. Man developed what little there is of his desire vehicle in the animal kingdom before beginning to make first attempts to attain his rightful place in the human kingdom. Animal passions still hold sway and manipulate man like a puppet. Only when he reaches into the higher unselfish regions of the desire world will he liberate himself.

The symptoms and rubrics in homœopathy considered to be mental are in fact mostly emotional and are correctly considered as most important. The conditions of love, jealousy, hate, grief, fear, pride, sadness, joy, anger, etc. have much power to uplift or degrade the life force and the various vehicles. Indifference or withdrawal from life is as carcinogenic in its nature as the most powerfully negative emotions.

It is in the desire world that we identify ourselves, for it is here that the consciousness is centred, at the present stage of evolution for ordinary man. Negative emotional activity will form the groove down which the toxins of destruction will pour, bringing forth disease, decay and corruption.

THE WORLD OF THOUGHT

In the seven sub-divisions of this region, the three higher ones are called the region of abstract thought. The four denser regions supply the mind-stuff in which we encapsulate and embody our ideas, this is the region of concrete thought. The world of thought is the central world of the five from which man obtains his vehicles. Here spirit meets body. It is the highest of the three worlds in which man's evolution is being carried forward at the present time, the two higher worlds being held in abeyance.

The region of concrete thought has the mind-stuff which clothes the ideas generated in the region of abstract thought. These then act as balance wheels and regulate the impulses generated in the desire world, as a result of impacts received from the world of form.

The archetypes of physical form in all its expressions are found in the lowest sub-division of concrete thought, the continental region. Here also is found the geography of the continents and islands, and they are fashioned accordingly. The archetypes are creative blueprints and they fashion all forms in the physical realm. Any geographical change must first be wrought in this region. When an architect wants to build a house, he first conceives it in his mind, this is his archetype, for he cannot build his house without first conceiving it thus. He clothes it in the mind-stuff from the lowest realm of concrete thought. It becomes a material idea. From there plans are drawn and the house built. The house is more solid and longer lasting in the realm of thought, for here it will stay for the rest of the man's life, enabling him to reproduce it at will, while at death it remains imprinted on the reflecting ether, and those that know how will have access to it. On the physical plane, however, the house may be destroyed by fire, flood, war, or decay.

The second sub-division, or oceanic region, is the region of etheric archetypes and is rich with flowing, pulsating life. All the forces which work through the four ethers have their origins here. It is a sparkling stream of flowing life, known in homœopathy as vital force, which animates all forms though their purpose and expression may be vastly different.

The third region is the aerial region, and here is found the archetype of all the desires, passions, wishes, feelings – emotions such as we experience in the desire world. All the activities of the desire world appear here as atmospheric conditions.

The fourth world is the region of archetypal force, the central and most important region of the five worlds in which man's entire evolution is worked. On one side of this kingdom are the three higher worlds – the world of abstract thought, the world of life spirit and the world of divine spirit. While on the other side are the three lower worlds – the world of concrete thought, the desire world and the physical world.

This fourth region of the mental body is a pivot, bounded by the realm of spirit on one side and the worlds of form on the other. Here spirit reflects itself in matter and is the house of archetypal forces which direct the activity of the archetypes in the region of concrete thought. From this region spirit works on matter in a formative manner.

The forms in the lower worlds are reflections of spirit in the higher worlds. All the forms and objects that we are familiar with in our own physical realm have their origin in pure spirit. It should be plain to see now that everything in the physical realm existed before it was clothed in physical matter and shaped by form to become the things which we know so well, much the same as we talk of ideas being clothed in the mind-stuff from the lower realms of thought, in order to give them expression.

The fifth region is reflected in the third region. The sixth region is reflected in the second region. The seventh region is reflected in the first region.The whole of the region of abstract thought is reflected in the world of desire.The world of the spirit is reflected in the etheric region.The world of divine spirit is reflected in the chemical region.

The world of divine spirit is the region of the highest spiritual influence in man. The crystals, minerals and gems in the solid realm of the chemical region are revered by healers for their powers. Cherished by many, their beauty is a constant source of wonder as only the highest hierarchies can work on the densest material.

The degree to which ideas generated in the world of abstract thought may become 'clothed' in form depends upon the amount of material built into the aura that we have taken the time to construct. This process is the active intellect and though important as a phase of development, is mistakenly revered by society as the highest form of human intelligence. The stumbling to greater progress lies in the pomposity which manifests with the idea and reveals the pride and conceit which exists in both group and individual nature. Here is the arrogance of ignorance often displayed by so-called experts, scientific or otherwise.

"You are now what you are because of what you have been", may be partly explained by the dependence on material we have worked into the aura. The same theme extends through all life and endeavours. It is what makes us what we are, different from our fellows yet similar in other respects. Feelings, desires, attitudes and all manner of emotion is worked into the aura. The greater the repetition (habit) the more it is worked in. What is in our aura is what we project into the world and by natural law it is what the world reflects back to us.

Medically speaking, the patient we see before us is the sum total of all they have been in the past. It is possible to observe all this without the use of word or brain. This explains the importance in homœopathy of prescribing on a patient's past, to clear from the being mistakes made and diseases suffered, thus changing habit and releasing them from the patterns of the past. This is not achieved with the use of one remedy or even two or three, but by a willingness to penetrate with understanding the patient's being.

As with all activity, with practice it works and grows, building into the prescriber's being new and more worthy activity, while weeding out the old outmoded habit of desire and idle 'thought'. This is using homœopathy as a tool of evolutionary progress.

Psychology attempts to deal with a person's past in order to heal and understand the present, as well as change the future. The symptoms displayed in the present moment will indicate to the prescriber the possible use of certain homœopathic remedies, which come from the four kingdoms of nature – mineral, vegetable, animal and human. Remedies from the first two kingdoms have their origins in past evolution and are indicated in the present because past activity, whilst evolving through a person, has been carried forward and represents the unwanted baggage we bring with us into this life. Remedies from the third kingdom also have their origins in the past, but not entirely, as man still has his being firmly rooted in the animal kingdom, whilst endeavouring to ennoble himself and rise above it into the human kingdom proper.

The function of the three worlds (the physical world, the desire world, and the world of thought) and the four kingdoms (the mineral kingdom, the vegetable kingdom, the animal kingdom and the human kingdom) may assist in the understanding of endeavour and the drama of life, of the nature and sequence of experience and its consequence and purpose.

In considering the vegetable kingdom and the animal and human kingdoms, the vegetable takes in carbon dioxide and puts out oxygen while the other two perform the reverse. Thus the planet and its life live off themselves and what they put into the atmosphere.

THE FOUR KINGDOMS

To exist in any of the four kingdoms it is necessary to have a vehicle composed of the material of that kingdom in order to express its qualities whilst being in the physical realm. In the invisible worlds are found the reason for man's ability to move, propagate, feel and think, while a plant may only grow and propagate. However, the dense bodies of mineral, plant, animal and man are all composed of the same chemical material. The etheric vehicle of the mineral does not possess a separate vital body and therefore it cannot grow, propagate or show life. The lowest of the four states of ether, the chemical, is active in the mineral. Its reflection in the realm of divine spirit through the chemical ether provides its great beauty and healing power.

The plant has a separate vital body as do animals and man. In the plant the chemical and the ethers only are active, providing its ability to assimilate and grow, whilst able to propagate its kind. The light ether is to some extent present but remains dormant. The reflecting ether is absent in the plant.

In the animal the chemical, life and light ethers are active giving it the powers to grow, propagate, generate heat and use the faculty of sense perception. The fourth ether remains inactive; it has no memory or thought – that which may appear as such is of a different nature.

In man all four ethers are active. Through the chemical ether he is able to grow, and propagate through the life ether. The light ether means he may generate heat in his dense body and work on the nerves and muscles. This work on the nerve and muscle fibres extends his power of communication in the world through the five senses, increasing activity and the power of assimilation of experience. The reflecting ether enables man to control his vehicles through thought. It also stores past experience as memory.

The substance we build in must be drawn from the various worlds as we live, experience and grow thereby. But since we may only draw upon our own, the amount available depends upon the amount of work we have done in a particular world, impressing on it the stamp of our being by our work. Every single living moment of now we are impressing some world, and in due season it will return to us bearing with it the nature of our stamp, depending on the mood we were in when we stamped it, and that mood's relationship to the mood in which we will use it on its return. Thus will it help or hinder us. This will turn the wheel of karma. The strong and the weak, the misshapen and the well formed, the diseased and the healthy, the idiot and the sage – all bear witness to their own endeavours.

This may seem harsh but it makes no judgement; the true healer seeks only the knowledge of cosmic law with love and endeavour and without sentimentality as an impulsive force. All the good reasons, excuses and explanations extended and offered must be set aside for the way things are speaks for itself. The law does not discriminate between who it likes and who it does not; it just is.

This should enable the student to begin to separate the excuse or specious reason from the reality whose origin is in the unseen realms, of which the subject under question will not be aware. In order to heal we must seek to perceive the activities behind the form. To work upon the form alone will not alter the unseen activity which spawned it. Just as we know that a wart is not a physical manifestation in itself or of itself, but is subject to the processes we know in homœopathy as sycosis, or the spirit of gonorrhoea, equally the entire manifestation of a human being is moulded in the three realms, living on the fruit of its own endeavour as it evolves through the four kingdoms.

The spirit's control of the vehicle is dependent on thought

which, in turn, is dependent on the reflecting ether's storage of experience as memory. The nature and accuracy of memory is dependent on understanding. Herein lies part of the eternal habitual cycle of what we build in, what we put out and what we receive back in the sequence of experiences we call life. Each is dependent on the other. Only conscious thought governed by vision on our own behalf will intervene and change the script or subconscious thought (karma).

As the dense body is built into the matrix of the vital body in the womb, the lines of force in the latter trace the physical form to an exact copy, apart from the differences already mentioned. Throughout the life the vital body builds and restores the dense form, counteracting the abuse to which the dense body is subject. Without this the dense body would quickly fall into decay. During sleep (the nearest state to death except coma) the higher vehicles leave the dense body; however, the vital vehicle or part of it remains, restoring the physical body ready for the next day's activity.

At death the vital body leaves the dense vehicle, passing control to the planetary forces working through the chemical ether, thereby restoring it to its primordial state through disintegration and decay.

The vital body is composed of millions of tiny points which enter and vitalise the hollow cavities of the dense atoms, setting them vibrating at a higher rate than that of the mineral. In drowning, falling or freezing the vital body leaves the dense vehicle rendering the atoms temporarily inanimate. Later it re-enters and the resistance of the atoms is the phenomenon we call pins and needles. It is the same when a limb goes to sleep.

In the ordinary man the vital body and dense body are closely interlocked; while in those who are psychic or clairvoyant, they are as a rule loosely connected, allowing reception on higher levels to take place – a faculty normally blocked by the brain. When involuntary and not understood it is the 'spaced outness' often experienced by sycotic subjects requiring MEDORRHINUM or THUJA, etc.. The focus in the brain (pituitary gland/brow centre) becomes diffused and the person is unable to concentrate properly or use the faculty of thought. The crown centre (pineal gland) however, remains active and receptive allowing clairvoyance to function. It is the bringing under conscious control which gives value to the faculty. In hypnosis part of the hypnotist's vital body is substituted for that of the recipient.

The true medium will use the crown chakra and qualities of the pineal gland while concentrating firmly in the brow centre (pituitary gland) in order to operate. The other glands will also be balanced. However, some mediums use the vital body as a vehicle for entities from the desire world to materialise. In this case the vital body oozes from the left side of the body through the spleen (the gate of the vital body). The vital forces then cannot flow through the body as they normally would and the medium becomes exhausted, often using stimulants to recover. This kind of mediumship is morbid and like the use of drugs, constitutes the counterfeit to reality.

The vital force may be observed psychically passing out through the dense body. In health this is in a straight line. In illness the lines are crumpled and bent, showing the lack of vitality.

After death the vital body and the dense body disintegrate synchronously. As with the amputated limb, the victim being able to feel the limb as if it were still there. Only the planetary ether accompanies the separated part. This connection between an amputated limb and its etheric double is felt regardless of distance.

A reflective medium between the planets of our solar system and humanity is provided by the life spirit in its direct connection with the vital force. As already stated, within the vital body lie the seven centres of power or chakras which in turn have a direct influence over the glands of personality – the endocrine glands. Each of these chakras comes under a certain planetary influence through the forces of the life spirit. Its qualities and associations are thus imbued in the individual and the group, accounting for much subconscious behaviour. "It is not the fault of the planets, dear Brutus, but that we are subject to them." (Julius Caesar)

This is how astrology works. The ancients (and Shakespeare) knew of these things. The vital body therefore is the best field of study for those interested in planetary influence.

We are now the sum total of all that we have been. The present state is the substance of the past built upon the past. As water freezes so the lines of force become visible in the ice. They weren't haphazardly created. They were there all the time; you just didn't see them. You traced the lines of force in the vital body to be physically reproduced in the womb. You are now tracing the lines of the future. As you are the past, so you will be the future. This illustrates the importance in homœopathy of prescribing on the history or aetiology of the patient, so that past mistakes are not built into the future, creating a lack of harmony or disease with future requirements. Those manifesting in the present should be clear to see.

Disease has been variously described as a lack of harmony with one's environment, a refusal to acknowledge the truth, a lack of integration with the needs of one's spirit, etc. All these in their various forms are true.

The vital body is as much a part of the physical realm as the dense body, the law here being inertia. The vital body therefore, while counteracting the processes of death in the physical vehicle, is itself just as hesitant to change. It endeavours to maintain an established pattern. As stated, the habits are stamped on the vital body; resistance to change being just as strong when trying to improve an established pattern. Constant repetition, discipline and persistence will bring changes. This does not imply strain or struggle, but gentle and steady application. Likewise, the life spirit does not discriminate; it learns by rote and just functions.

The intellectual soul is the product of this activity. If you feed the brain on rubbish then that is what it will reproduce, to be stamped upon the reflecting ether and extended into the world thereby. But if thought is ennobled and the capacity for it deliberately increased through greater activity in the world (desire body), then experience, understanding and wisdom will be its fruit, increasing that quality we know as intelligence.

In hypnotism substance from the operator is projected into the subject's being, with all its vices and virtues. Where vice meets vice or virtue meets virtue, there is a strengthening. Where vice meets virtue there is a weakening. The power is gained as the subject uses it for his own purposes, rather like the arc of a coil to boost electric current. Thus stamped, the new lot gathers substance of a like kind as it goes back to devastate he who sent it out. All ungracious thoughts directed towards others have a similar process and likewise the goodwill of the prescriber will travel with the patient. In this lies a hint at the nature of the saying, "It matters not what the therapy is; it is the therapist that is important." As a healer, one's own condition, physically emotionally and mentally, is directly involved.

Both minerals and plants lack a separate dense vehicle; they are permeated only by the planetary desire body. Without this it is impossible to register feeling, desire or emotion. When a stone is broken it is the planetary desire vehicle, the spirit of the earth, which feels, the stone having no separate desire body. When a person injures themselves it is the person that feels the pain not the injured part, as that has no separate desire body. The planetary desire body permeates animal and humanity in the same way as it does stone and plant, but in addition animals and humans have a separate desire vehicle.

In the animal the desire body is built entirely of substance from the denser regions of the desire world. While in humanity a little of the substance from the more refined regions of desire are beginning to constitute the desire body. Purer material from the higher realms replaces that of the lower as humanity purifies its desires and ennobles its emotions.

As it is refined, the desire body grows in size, it does not assume the shape of the vital or physical bodies but does so after death. There is in it no settled place for any particle as there is in the dense body; it has no organs as do the dense and vital bodies; but there are centres of perception which remain in the same relative position to the etheric body. In most people these are latent.

These centres may be awakened according to response. A negative development causes an anti-clockwise vortex; a positive development gives a clockwise vortex, resulting in conscious control rather than passive submission. Negatively we observe ourselves as the world reflects back at us like a mirror, or we remain solely subject to planetary influence. Positively we see and investigate at will (desire force of attraction).

The root of the desire body is in the liver, that of the vital body in the spleen. Because of its power and state of disorganisation, most disease originates in the desire body, correspondingly affecting the liver. This not only explains why the organ appears as the centre of metabolism but also that it is implicated in so many disease processes. Everything in the desire body is registered in the liver. The currents flow out from the liver to the limits of the desire body and back again to the liver, fuelled by the feelings, emotions and passions which reach outward into the world with desire.

When an organism has developed sufficiently for the spirit to draw into its vehicles, then the currents are directed outward and there is the beginning of passionate life and warm blood. It is the warm red blood in the liver, sufficiently evolved to accommodate an indwelling spirit, which energises the outgoing currents of desire stuff. This causes the animal or man to display desire and passion.

Where there is vitality and motion but no red blood the creature has no separate desire body, is transitional between plant and animal and is moved by group spirit only. In cold-blooded creatures which have a liver and red blood there is a separate desire body and the group spirit directs the currents inward, as in their case the separate spirit is entirely outside the individual dense vehicle. Until the points of the vital body and the dense body correspond the spirit is not entirely indwelling.

In the realm of feeling and who feels, we touch upon responsibility and integrity of both the individual and the group towards each other and the environment; an issue which is just beginning to impinge upon man's consciousness. Yet the attitude prevailing in the world is to let the other person do it while we are left free to indulge our habits. Knowledge and understanding should begin to make a difference.

As man pollutes and degrades his environment in a selfish desire to exploit for commercial gain, the minerals he mines or the forests he chops down do not feel, but the planetary spirit suffers the consequences. Animals and human beings thus affected do feel. Industrial waste, nuclear science and cars create such a change to the environment that the planetary spirit must take action to redress the balance. Likewise we do the same to our own bodies promoting, largely through ignorance, health or disease. The homœopathic treatment that redresses the balance is often accompanied by aggravation and upheaval as the consequences are felt.

The human body is the temple of an indwelling spirit and we choose to wreck it. Responsibility to ourselves and our fellows is implied here; the aspiration and desire to serve of the student physician must be genuine and practical. "Am I my brother's keeper?", is an ignored phrase which takes on a mantle of reality.

Humanity is under consideration to see whether it is a suitable vehicle for the advance of evolving life. The wanton destruction presently occurring is not a positive argument in its favour. Homœopathy is a tool promoting that advance, not only individually, but on a group level. It is important therefore that each practice in their own way, so that all aspects of life and its needs may be advanced. As each generation of wonder drugs is developed and promoted so consequent disease and suffering is increased, leaving those who can think in search of some alternative. Man's responsibility to himself and to his environment must grow, at least as fast as his weapons and technology.

The refining of a vehicle is the result of activity in a particular realm. Everything follows the law of sequence, there is no evading or skipping of a stage. It is not possible to take the Kingdom of God by storm, however noble the desire or pure the aspiration. What we have is the ever-present moment of now and our conditions within it. There is no sudden enlightenment, it is an ever-evolving process. By the use of homœopathy the patient must travel through various stages in order to reach the point of health or cure. Any by-passing of a stage will leave the work undone and the patient subject to some kind of relapse or regression. Each stage is indicated by another remedy requiring a different response from the patient, thus promoting through natural sequence the state of liberation we call health. One of these remedies will be the constitutional, but that alone and prescribed in isolation is not enough to undertake this process. Likewise there is no fixed shape to the form of firmly-rooted health until there is an established pattern of behaviour in the appropriate realm or at each stage of treatment of the patient. There are no organs without organised living in the realm relevant to the body in question.

The law of sequence is a fundamental law of nature; ignorance of it is a main cause of frustration in homœopathic prescribing, especially among the various schools, each of which considers its method as the only way, and superior to all others. Orderly progress and sequence come from orderly living. Health cannot be encouraged if the life is fundamentally disordered, however good the reasons or excuses.

There are those who aspire to do good and to serve their fellows. They ask "What shall we do?". The answer is "What can you do?". You will do whatever tasks you have made yourself fit for, no more no less. How can those who aspire to healing give advice and good service to others if their own lives are chaotic and disordered? The established order requires radical reform, not least in the field of medicine. But we may only start from where we are now; outright rejection of everything and dropping out of the system is not the answer, but the proper and disciplined attention to the task in hand is. In order to aspire to any level, the work has to be done to get there.

The diseases of the animal kingdom are the most recently acquired by man as his passage through the mineral and vegetable kingdoms preceded this stage. With the introduction of a desire body and warm blood in the liver, the power to produce devastating diseases is much greater. Venereal diseases and their consequence down the generations are spawned in this realm. Man is still in the animal realm, he has not yet successfully aspired to the human kingdom. He drags with him the dross of earlier incarnations as well as errors made in those.

Here we may realise in homœopathy the huge importance of the disease nosodes (MEDORRHINUM, SYPHILINUM, etc.) in releasing man's body and spirit from animal disease (miasms) permitting in turn greater and easier access to those previously acquired in the mineral and vegetable kingdoms.

If disease of the animal realm is not successfully dealt with the integrity of the vehicles of human expression could be compromised. The use of pleasure drugs and the consequent lack of responsibility to one's fellows and environment must be stopped if any progress is to be made. In homœopathy the next stage is indicated by the next remedy. The achievement of each stage is dependent on the one before. The development of the patient is not possible out of its proper time and sequence. You may choose to give a number of different remedies but the next one is the one indicated and will bring the patient to the next stage. The next stage is the only one possible for achievement.

Minerals, plants and animals lack a vehicle correlating them to the world of thought. The highest domesticated animals may at first appear to have this faculty, but theirs is different and likened to a highly charged electric wire being brought close to another wire. Man is individualised, he has the power of thought. Animals, plants and minerals are not and are divided into species.

Man has an individual indwelling spirit, while there is one group spirit common to all animals and plants of the same species. All matter is crystallised spirit and the group spirits have crystallised out for themselves the dense material bodies of the different kingdoms. It is the group spirit which emanates and moves the dense vehicles. Only man has the complete chain of vehicles correlating to all divisions of the three worlds.

When an animal in one part of the world is observed to do something while another of the same species does something similar, it is evidence of the group spirit wrestling with its individual vehicles. Likewise, the annual migration of birds in perfect formation and timing is the organisation by the group spirit of its subjects.

The animal lacks one link, the mind. The plant lacks two, the mind and desire vehicle; while the mineral lacks three, mind, desire body and vital body. Man is increasing his level of consciousness by descending into the chemical region and marshalling his various vehicles, learning to bring them under control and wield them to some creative effect.

The desire body has no organs. The mind is the last to be developed and is not yet considered a body, but is a link through which the ego may focus upon the brain. A vehicle without organs is by itself useless as an instrument of consciousness. Only through their link to the well organised dense body are the higher vehicles of any value. The physical body is the most perfect of man's vehicles so far, being the best organised. The vital body is nearly as perfectly organised, while the desire and mental vehicles are just clouds.

The group spirit functioning in a spiritual body has its lowest vehicle in the desire world. The animal the dense body, vital body and desire body, but the group spirit which directs it is outside; the vital body and desire body of the animal are not entirely within the dense body, especially where the head is concerned.

Within the vehicle in which the group spirit functions is a varying number of virgin spirits, themselves possessing the consciousness of the group spirit. The group spirit directs the vehicles built by the virgin spirits, caring for others and helping them to evolve their vehicles. As they evolve so does the group spirit.

The spirit of the animal is not yet individualised and therefore remains separate from the physical vehicle, being part of a self-conscious entity of a different evolution: the group spirit. As the virgin spirits evolve so they become more self conscious and the grip of the group spirit is lessened; they become the humanity of their day. They manifest greater will of their own, becoming increasingly responsible for their own actions and gaining more freedom from the group spirit. The group spirit will influence them to a lesser degree as races, tribes, family or community spirit. This is known in psychology as group mind or group consciousness. When each individual has become totally responsible and capable of acting in full harmony with cosmic law the ego will be entirely free of group spirit.

The stamp of the family or group implies group behaviour, activity on an automatic (unconscious) level. With the use of homœopathy we endeavour to free the patient of unthinking activity, pointing them ever towards individual thought and action. Family and group karma (miasms) may be removed from an individual or a whole generation, freeing them from outside suggestion and liberating the power of inner authority. This is what is intended for mankind, to be free to do as he wills to an ever increasing degree as he progresses. He must become a law unto himself.

The group spirit of the mineral has its lowest vehicle in the region of abstract thought, and is therefore three steps removed from its dense vehicle, hence it is in a state of trance like unconsciousness. The mineral kingdom, having no individual vital body, cannot be the vehicle for currents belonging to the higher realms. The group spirit of the plant kingdom has its lowest vehicle in the region of concrete thought. It is two stages removed from its dense vehicle, consequently plants have a consciousness corresponding to that of dreamless sleep.

Man sees things outside himself in sharp distinct outlines. Animals have an internal picture consciousness similar to the dream state, accompanied by an impression that the object is beneficial or otherwise to its well-being. This passive state of consciousness renders it easy for the group spirit to manifest by suggestion as animals have no will of their own. A vehicle for the expression of an individual spirit must have three things: an upright walk, an upright larynx (only such a larynx is capable of speech) and warm blood.

Consider well the implications of group activity and the group spirit. Whatever study group or clan you may be in, you are endeavouring to integrate and demonstrate the power of the group. Trying to remain separate or lacking the courage to speak up when inspiration demands it is non-integration, leading to dis-integration. The cells forming the various organs of your body all work together for the good of the whole, thus creating the organ. The organs work together to form a body. Any selfishness or non-participation creates disease (cancer) and renders the level of organ function impossible. The integrity breaks down.

It is not possible for any one person to know all of homœopathy, its range or power, but each member of the group will add their knowledge in their particular individual way, so that each contribution to the group will create a greater knowledge which everyone may draw on as they will. Fear and pride are the dragons to be slain here and their presence to a greater or lesser extent is in everyone. The field of homœopathy is ideal for this work as its influence is limitless. The patient and the prescriber have limitations but homœopathy does not.

Obsession with minimum standards of practice to appease the wrath of a bureaucratic god is to sacrifice the miracle of one's individuality upon the altar of mediocrity. One's individual contribution to the group is one way of rising above this mundane level. Members of a properly integrated group are the virgin spirits, forerunners of a new creation on a higher level of being. They are in fact virgin spirits on that level.

We talk of individuality and the group. Although to many these two states may seem incompatible or even diametrically opposed, they are in fact quite compatible. It only seems impossible because they have not yet been achieved. It is both these qualities which in the New Age will be the focus of advance. A proper individualisation, as opposed to a herd, freely functioning within an integrated group is the goal.

Man and his vehicles evolve and develop through a series of stages, following a definite sequence. It is knowledge of this sequence and adherence to it that negates the necessity of karma being used as a guide to keep the individual on the path. Disease and unhappy lives are the consequence of deviation from the programme. Once we begin to take on the idea we develop a feel for it, adjusting the course as necessary.

This system, it will be observed, is strictly interlocking. Each grade is dependent upon the one beneath for the material for its present stage of development, at the same time being dependent on the one above for the impulsion or inspiration. We are all tied up in one huge parcel, no-one gets out as separate from anyone else and the pace at the top is governed by the level of achievement at the bottom. Exploitation therefore of any lower group or grade is counterproductive and is a very bad bargain in the great surge forward. Those who wantonly plunder the four kingdoms would do well to think of this.

THE EGO

The individual spirit or ego functions directly within the subtle substance of the region of abstract thought – in so far as our past efforts have worked that substance into our own individual aura. From there it views the impact and effect upon the vital body of information received through the five senses, and the reactions in the desire body generated by them, and mirrored in the mind; the process we like to call thought. In this largely unconscious cycle it may be well to remember the role of the liver and its diseases, it being the root or gateway of the desire body.

From these mental impressions and images we form, in the substance of the region of abstract thought, our conclusions and many of our attitudes, judgements, etc. concerning the subjects with which we deal. This bears much thought. What is the subject matter? On what do you feed your brain and five senses? Indulgence in low or unworthy activity, placing oneself in an environment where the impacts from without come from the trash cans of human activity will encourage morbid emotional responses, leading to twisted, devious and narrow conclusions and attitudes. Such will wander the back alleys of human experience, the arrogance of ignorance ensuring they see no further. Only karma creating crisis will stimulate the move to more worthwhile activity. This unworthiness is purely a personal matter, since we all have our own standards generated from within. This generating authority from within is far preferable to the hypocrisy of a morality generated from outside. Consider here the section on the desire body and the benefits of positive activity in this area.

Conclusions resulting from habitual activity so far described, are ideas. These ideas are projected through the mind using will as a vehicle. Here it takes concrete shape as a thought form by clothing itself in mind stuff from the region of concrete thought. The mind projects the image in one of three directions according to the will or habit of the thinker.

Firstly, against the desire body in order to arouse feeling leading to action. If the thought is met by interest then one of the twin forces of attraction or repulsion will be motivated. Attraction arouses a centripetal force or energy which throws the thought into the desire body, endows it with added life like an electric coil, increases the current and clothes it with mind stuff. The thought will then act upon the etheric brain and propel the vital force through the appropriate brain centres along the nerves to the voluntary muscles, thus creating the necessary action upon an idea. Here the vital force is used as a vehicle for the idea to create action. Greater vitality in life produces more creative thought and activity; action follows thought. The force in the thought is expended, the image remains on the reflecting ether of the vital body as memory of the act and the feeling that caused it.

This could be reproduced by the spirit from this filing cabinet at any time in the future when any previous experience is required in facing a particular situation. If the previous experience be a painful or unfortunate one, the natural reaction or habit of the person will be to shy away from the impending new experience, arousing the force of repulsion in the desire body. However, lessons learned in the mind through the power of thought (for those who use it), may adjust the reaction and behaviour around the activity, producing a more positive result and building that into the ether. So we grow and develop our intelligence. This process requires active thought on our own behalf and not left merely to habit. If habit takes over, fear will rule. Knowledge banishes fear but it must be knowledge based on the fruits of personal experience.

If repulsion is aroused, there will be a struggle between the spiritual force (the will) within the thought form, and the desire body. This is the battle between conscience and desire, the higher and lower nature. The spiritual force in the face of resistance, will seek to clothe the thought form in the necessary desire stuff required to manipulate the brain and voluntary muscles. The force of repulsion will endeavour to scatter the material and oust the thought. If the spiritual energy is strong enough, it will force its way through to the brain centres and whilst maintaining its desire stuff will manipulate the vital force, compelling action, and will then leave a vivid record of the struggle on the memory.

If the spiritual energy is weak or exhausted, the force of repulsion will overcome it, the material scattered and the thought ousted. It will be stored in the memory as are all thought forms once their energy is expended. If the thought form is met with indifference it may leave a weak impress on the reflecting ether after its energy has been exhausted.

Secondly, if no immediate action is required by the impacts from without or the mental images generated thereby, these, together with the accompanying thoughts, may be projected directly on the reflecting ether to be used at some future date. The power of observation and conscious memory are required here. As no action has been taken there is no experience to build in as a direct result. The ego through the mind has instant access to this filing cabinet.

Ideas resurrected and imbued with new spiritual force gain in strength, vividness and efficiency, more readily ensuring action on their particular lines. Generating deliberate conscious thought produces ideas and although these ideas may not require immediate action, the degree and quality of the thought produces a rich storehouse of ideas for future activity, which will themselves attract the circumstances for their own manifestation. Again, it is the deliberate conscious activity replacing idle habit and enriching the life experience and intelligence.

Thirdly, the thought form may be projected towards another mind to act as a suggestion, to carry information, etc. or it may be directed against the desire body of another person to compel action, as in the case of hypnotism from a distance. It will then act in the same manner as if it were the victim's own thought. (This may happen involuntarily as when a number of people receive the same idea at roughly the same time. This can easily be observed in the commercial world.) When the purpose of such a projected thought form has been completed or its energy expended in unsuccessful attempts to achieve its end, the thought form gravitates back to its creator, bearing with it the indelible record of its journey and activity. Its success or failure is imprinted on the negative atoms of the reflecting ether of its creator's vital body. Here it forms that part of the record of the thinker's life which is known as the sub-conscious mind. This record is much more important than the one to which we have conscious access.

The ether contained in the air we breathe carries with it a detailed and accurate picture of the conditions existing each moment in the aura. The slightest thought, feeling or emotion is transmitted immediately to the lungs and injected into the blood. Blood is one of the highest products of the vital body and it is the direct vehicle of the ego. The pictures it contains are impressed on the negative atoms of the vital body, to serve as arbiters of one's destiny in the post mortem state.

Man's mind, such as it is, is a jungle, the recycling plant of undisciplined, vague and unenlightened emotion, and makes for a poor mirror. The importance of the deliberate cultivation of a quiet mind should now be a little more obvious. The emotions as they exist are the result of vague and inaccurate impressions, subsequent interpretation bears little relation to reality leaving conclusions at fault. And how dogmatic and fixed we can be concerning these conclusions! It is well for the therapist to study this in himself and in those who seek assistance.

This twisted heap of habitual activity is the direct cause of most disease, one's personal compost, there to be studied by all who can read. The attitude of detachment is the greatest help we may give ourselves in the study of this process and our endeavours to change it through helping ourselves. The point of intervention is after the impact upon the vital body through the five senses and before emotional reaction sets in. There is a moment of stillness where we may decide to react in the same habitual way (unconscious) or deliberately bring about an action of our own choice (conscious). A degree of detachment is needed to perceive this moment thus creating the opportunity for choice.

Knowing oneself, and the cleansing of the mind, is contained here if these processes are studied and properly understood. For this is the anatomy and physiology of man's vehicles, laying before you the mechanics of evolution whereby you may intervene on your own behalf, making your journey along the thread of conscious life smoother, happier and more rapid.

The study of homœopathic remedies should now take on a different dimension and meaning. The thread of continuity will become more apparent and ideas barely touched upon may be elaborated, bringing an understanding of the materia medica way beyond the printed word. Reasons for prescribing may not be based on mundane materia medica alone, excellent though it is, but upon enlightened visions which will produce results so far unthought of or undreamed of. Homœopathy has no limits. It is those who use it, both in the giving and receiving, who are alone limited. Homœopathy is a young art and the processes mentioned here are just one of the ways it must be developed for future needs – the needs of those who are yet to come and are reliant on our work now.

An understanding of the processes involved enriches the possibility of cleansing disease patterns which are ever more complicated. Adherence to the original idea as laid down is not enough in itself but is more than excellent as a sound base for future construction, which does not devalue the original concept. This is the bare bones; it is up to each to bring it alive through individual understanding and endeavour. Then how much more powerful will be the human race to heal itself.

Our memory, both conscious and sub-conscious, relates in its entirety to the experiences of this life only. It is the record of impressions and events imprinted on the vital body. These may be changed or completely eradicated from the ether of the vital body.

In addition to this, there is a superconscious memory. It is the filing cabinet of all faculties developed and all knowledge acquired in previous lives. This record is indelibly engraved on the life spirit. Knowledge here does not mean the academic type gained from books, but knowledge as the fruit of experience. The superconscious memory need not clothe itself in mind-stuff or desire-stuff in order to manifest. It may not always need to expose itself to the process of reasoning. In this way the superconscious memory is able to take action in a direction which may seem illogical to those in observance, yet to the spirit is wholly the correct line to take.

REBIRTH

During waking hours the activity of the mind and desire vehicles are constantly breaking down the dense vehicle – every thought, every moment, breaks down physical tissue. The vital body faithfully endeavours to rebuild and restore what the other vehicles are breaking down.

It should now begin to be seen how homœopathic treatment works on the vital body (vital force), assisting it to direct its forces most efficiently in areas of greatest need. There is and will be a legacy of ill-gotten fruits from the undisciplined mind and desire vehicles, breaking down tissue and creating chaos at a faster rate than the vital body is able to rebuild. Homœopathy goes some considerable way to redress the balance, and at the same time change or eradicate the memory from the reflecting ether. This is one of the reasons why aggravations of symptoms, or otherwise uncomfortable experiences are undergone during homœopathic treatment. The vital body is changing and altering its vehicles accordingly, from disease to health.

Note that the vitality is used as a vehicle for ideas garbed in mind-stuff and desire-stuff, compelling action; those observed to undergo improved health with treatment become more active, mostly but not wholly along their right line of advance. Not all purges, however, are visible, except as a definite increase in the level of health and well-being. A change in the contents of, or an eradication from, the reflecting ether through homœopathic prescribing is like a shadow passing from the being, leaving a marked increase in health. This may or may not require the experience of acute illness to accompany its passage.

The activity of the vehicles during sleep forms the basis for the activity of the following day. The activity of the ego during the period from death to rebirth forms the basis for the activity during the following incarnation.

At death, the vital body, the desire body and the mind leave the dense body with a spiral movement, taking with them the soul of one dense atom. This imprint, or soul, of a dense atom is called the seed atom. The seed atom has remained stable in every physical vehicle ever used by the ego. In life it is situated in the left ventricle of the heart near the apex. At death it rises to the brain by way of the pneumo-gastric nerve leaving with the higher vehicles by way of the sutures between the parietal and occipital bones.

When the spirit slowly withdraws from its vehicles, as in cases of lingering but terminal disease, the seed atom will rise to the head, lodging itself for the time being in the pineal gland. This accounts for the often remote or spaced out nature of those due to die soon. The seed atom is personal, as each physical vehicle is individual according to he who built it. In the advent of heart transplant surgery, this gives rise to much interesting thought and speculation.

The silver cord connecting the vehicles does not break until the person has viewed the panorama of his past life which is contained within the vital body. Cremation of the physical body speeds the disintegration of the vital body. When a man dies his release restores to some extent his spiritual power and he can read the pictures of his life on the negative field of the reflecting ether of his vital body like a movie screen (the seat of the sub-conscious memory). The whole of his past life passes before him in reverse order. The essence of the experience is imprinted on his higher vehicles, in due season to manifest in the next life as right feeling and conscience. This activity may last from a few hours to several days until the endurance of the vital body has reached its limit.

On reaching its limit, the vital body collapses and terminates the panorama and forces the man to withdraw into the desire world. The silver cord snaps and the vital body returns to the dense body, but no longer interpenetrates it, just hovers over it, decaying synchronously with the dense vehicle. While he is viewing the panorama of past events the man is, of course, attached to his vital body and therefore also to his physical body. Consequently, any post mortem, surgical activity or plundering the physical vehicle for its organs causes much distress to the person if occurring within three days following of death. For this reason, in the ancient world and in some modern societies, cremation does not take place until three days after death.

The processes are much the same when leaving the vital body as they were leaving the dense body. The life forces of one atom are taken to be used as a nucleus for the next vital body. Thus man enters the desire world with two seed atoms, those of the dense, and vital bodies, together with the desire body and the mind.

If he could leave all desires of the material world behind, the desire body would very quickly fall away from him, leaving him free to proceed to what is called the heaven world. As long as he retains the desires of the earthly life he must remain in his desire body. Those who have indulged heavily in drugs or alcohol and those who cling longingly to their material wealth will remain longer here. Desires can be indulged by induction; a drunk may receive a kind of satisfaction from the bodies of drinkers drinking, likewise with drug addicts. It is not from alcohol itself but only the vibrations of an indulging body that will serve his purpose. To the clairvoyant the sight around bars and pubs is not a pretty one.

Changing the impressions stored in the vital body is likened to the process of the drowning man: the man wants nothing so much as air. The process is not for the conventionally minded or for those who make themselves reliant on social handouts. It is not for the materialist or for those who would shore up the pillars of society. The law of matter is inertia and the resistance to change is strong. The vital body is programmed and reacts accordingly. It has no inherent resistance of its own, and once reprogrammed it will function in cooperation with the new pattern.

It is easier for the clairvoyant who is genuinely spiritually minded to change the impressions stored in the vital body, as with them the vehicles are looser and therefore more malleable. In the materialist or conventionalist the vehicles are likely to be impacted, more rigid and resistant to change. In the latter type such change and its necessity would not enter the consciousness. It takes the courage of one who is prepared to go against the flow of conventionalism, to place one's head on the chopping block of divine discontent and not only survive but live according to one's own inner demands, pointing the way for others by personal example.

"Give up all thou hast and follow me", is not a meaningless concept. Neither does it involve following a popular guru, however convincing his credentials. It involves laying the foundation of one's own inner authority. To "follow me" is to recognise the God within and entails taking time to listen, establishing the link and living one's life accordingly. As ever, man gropes around in the world of physical phenomena for answers that are within. Constant habitual activity will establish a pattern and only mindful application will change it. Steady application and effort without strain is the keynote. It is the regularity that counts. Better to make five minutes effort a day than two hours at the end of the month. It is not an external study as with academic learning, but a twenty-four hours a day state of existence through the ever-moving moment of now, encompassing many incarnations upon the thread of consciousness.

Living in the physical world we are subject to its impact on our, as yet, unrefined desire body, and most fall down heavily in this area, building in much desire relevant only to the plane of physical existence which, if we are to move on, goes the way of all flesh and falls away from us. Such activity must be relinquished as it has no relevance beyond the desire world.

The three lower regions of the desire world are called purgatory (a place of purging). As fire will consume the physical body (cremation), so will it also consume the desire attached to its plane of existence. Christians perverted this into threats of hellfire and eternal damnation, used as a weapon to induce fear among people thus rendering them passive and controllable. However, this doesn't work these days and power has passed to the medical authorities who make similar threats, with equally effective results.

During this stage man is free of his physical body. His brain and sympathetic nervous system are no longer able to throw up a smokescreen of excuses and justifications, allowing the man to massage his conscience into slumber. Here he will indulge his full range of feelings as he views the panorama of his past life rolling backwards before him. The mythology and feeling around the word purgatory is reflective of the judgement man puts upon himself. While reviewing his past activities from a more detached viewpoint, it is to act as a guide to right activity in the future, there being no question of a jealous god seeking punishment or retribution.

The memory of individual experiences is forgotten but the feeling remains as essence from the review and is stamped on the seed atom of the desire body. During the next incarnation the script unfolds and this essence becomes the still, small voice in the background, rarely heeded, castigated as illogical by a conventional brain reflecting a society built upon expedience. The greater the impact of the panorama at the time of review, the more indelible the stamp and the louder the voice, more clearly to be heard. If this voice is loud, and the stubborn determination to ignore it greater, it will manifest as conscience, followed by the prickly feeling and fidgeting of endocrine activity, reflecting itself on the brain as justification for the action taken. The cultivation of this voice may be acted on now by reviewing, at the end of the day, the events of the day in reverse order. Working on the link between cause and effect can give much insight into the results of an activity and strengthen the reflective power which eventually, if persisted in, may not be limited to the recall of a day, but extended deeper into the past. This practice can reduce the amount of time spent in purgatory.

The area called the first heaven comprises the three upper regions of the desire world and it is here that the results of man's sufferings are built into the seed atom of the desire body, together with a feeling for what is right, to be used as our aid to correct activity and decision in future lives. This region is known as the Summerland and is an area of development and progress for those who have been studious, artistic or altruistic.

The physical world is the world of form; the desire world is the world of colour; the thought world is the world of tone.

Man now has three seed atoms, the ego clothed only in the vagueness of mind; the desire body is left to decay as were the previous two, each leaving their forces contained within the seed atom.

The cosmos is composed of spirit and matter in various forms of existence, according to the cycle. Matter is crystallised spirit. Force is the same spirit but not yet crystallised. Crystallisation is spirit becoming matter. Decay is matter becoming spirit. This should give a different point of view to the passing of life. The process of death is not the dramatic ending of everything, as we have been educated to believe, but the passing from one state of consciousness to another, discarding vehicles that are no longer of use, as we leave the realm for which they were fitted. Nothing in the universe is wasted, all is recycled, an idea which man is only just beginning to embrace, on the lowest level. However, "as above, so below", the connection to be made in due season, no doubt. Furthermore, everything that is cycled and recycled is improved and upgraded while the little minds of men are consumed in their everyday dramas.

It is currently fashionable amongst some who grope for spiritual advance to suppress or attempt to ignore desire. It should now be apparent that it is a very necessary facility, helping man in the course of his evolution. It is the nature and quality of the desire indulged that creates so much trouble. It is not material things in the material world which are to blame for our materialism, but our relationship to them. Desire quickly becomes covetousness, needs are superseded by greed, while the rest of Pandora's box is buried by the glutton.

The physical plane of existence has its requirements, its needs, and it is the duty of each of us to provide for self and family in order to maintain the physical vehicle in some dignity and good health. This should, having been established, provide a foundation for the expression of the spirit towards meeting the purpose of the incarnation. However, with most the record gets stuck, the providing for needs accelerates into avarice and the materialist imagines he knows what life is about. If man cannot raise himself and use aspiration as a vehicle of evolution then the forces will use what he makes available – money and materialism will become the apparatus of development. One may observe this by the publication in recent years of developmental books focussing on money making. Alternative book shops are full of the ambitious.

To look at it from another point of view: provision in any realm is always made to meet the appetites of that realm. Nature is all-embracing, she will not create appetite and neglect to provide for her children in any respect. But man, as yet, has little awareness of evolution, provision or spirit. He imagines himself to be alone and therefore must defend himself.

It is a law: all that is needed will be provided, but to embrace this as a living phenomena (and thus build it in as knowledge), requires the courage and foresight to break from conformity and "do only what thine own heart commands". The voice in the background will not be quieted, and resistance to its demands result in much disease. Conventional society views life differently, building a wall of death between itself and its creator, while making provisions for disaster and war. If we as individuals had the vision to perceive and enact what each of us came here to do, the pain and suffering of compulsion (karma) would be far less necessary.

The other torment which goads man in purgatory is also self-inflicted. He passes judgement on himself through his own mental and emotional reactions to the panorama of his past life. He is alone, there is no judge and jury poised to condemn him. It is his own mental and emotional habits, and how he falls below his own standards, from which he suffers. There is no conventional society or religion here pointing the finger at him. He is left with his own inner standards, such as he has made his own. He stands up naked, before himself, with no brain or endocrine glands to soothe his conscience or justify his actions. He is in the rarefied atmosphere of perfect honesty.

How much better it would have been for him to have acted according to his own knowledge and judgement – his own inner authority, and now he sees how shamefully he has fallen as the vision of his past life grinds on without let or mercy. He will wish he had cultivated detachment and impersonality, enabling him to build in corrections without torment.

The authority within is an aspect at present focussed on by the forces of evolution, as wilful children make their own judgements and adolescents leave the nest for some early learning in self-reliance. The young resist the imposition of authority without. There are casualties, but vision of the long term point of view and purpose could provide the impetus for their care and reinstatement. The socialist ideal could successfully embrace this path.

Consider the implication of the seed-atom. The seed contains within it the blueprint of its own script; given the right conditions it will grow and unfold accordingly. To this end all that is needed is provided.

The atom is neither wholly force nor matter. It cannot be seen however powerful the microscope, but may be observed only in motion by the radiating trail it creates. It is in a perpetual state of motion but in combination with other atoms it disappears into the molecule. The molecule may be observed – as the beginning of material phenomena, but not the atom. If the atom breaks away it may once again only be observed by its radiant trail. Atoms vary and move differently according to the nature and quality of the force with which they are imbued or part of.

It has been stated that the vital body penetrates the hollow centres of the atoms comprising the dense vehicles. The quality and power of the vital body is built and controlled by our every action, thought and emotion. Notice how we will feel weak, tired and lethargic when we are negative or depressed. Habitual indulgence in negative emotion will stunt the vital body in its growth and activity. Note, on the other hand, how positive emotional activity and thought will energise us. Engendering positive emotions within the desire body will empower the vital body. The vital body in turn will act as the vehicle of thought (as a result of ideas) and desire, thrusting both through the atoms of the brain, down the nerves and into the voluntary muscles to generate action.

This is the mechanics of life itself. At this point of evolution we are working on our various vehicles and aspects of them, including the vital body. This vehicle is becoming more powerful and seeks an ever more developed nervous system and muscular system to manifest through. It is the evolutionary process of making man a more powerful and effective being. Let us hope his sense of responsibility and vision develop at least as fast.

The atoms vibrate according to the power and quality of vitality within them. We have also seen that the reflecting ether of the vital body contains within it a record of every thought, emotion and action through the whole of the life. Therefore, it is our individual vitality which permeates every atom of our bodies. It is what we have made it, and what we are making it at this moment. It is the carrier of all the good we have imparted to it, and all the evil with which it has been engendered, according to our activity – not somebody else's. It also carries with it disease, so it may also permeate every atom, molecule and cell of our bodies, illustrating the folly of treating the part, without considering the whole of the being from a healing viewpoint. Positive thought and emotional activity, therefore, will provide greater vitality, health and well-being, from the atom to the totality of the being, each unit uniting with other units on its level, to form a group, in turn forming the single unit on the next level up, and so on.

The ancients knew about atoms, their qualities and behaviour. The ancient Egyptians had enough information to make a nuclear bomb, but their minds were not morbid, they had no need for it. However, they were not stressed by material structure in attempting to explain matter in terms of itself. They identified the atom as radiance, by its qualities, not by physical appearance. Now we may see that the vibrant personality, the radiant presence, the attraction and radiance of the true healer, have a cold scientific explanation. Always, we make ourselves what we are.

We may observe, those of us who have lived a few years, how life has become more intense and vital, how we must take in more information at a greater pace and learn how to use it, as the powers of evolution turn the screw. It is possible to notice by watching an old television programme of say twenty-five years ago, how much less vital are the characters compared with today, how sluggish are the course of events running through the plot. We are building and developing our vital bodies, nervous and muscular systems. In the last decade sport has become a major preoccupation for the group on a national level and for western societies as a whole. Its importance has grown and greater opportunities for all to partake have been presented. What may appear as the absurdity of possessing and manipulating a ball of a certain size in a sporting ritual, has as its basis a most sound purpose.

Consider again the behaviour of the atom, separate and in a state of perpetual motion, then appearing in combination; on separation again it takes up the state of vibration and radiation in space. In combination atoms form their group, working one hundred percent for the good of that group. The atom is in a state of liberty. Ideas around liberty, emancipation, freedom, rights and their sisters – responsibility and discipline – give much food for thought here, together with the question, "why does God allow such things to happen?".

These ideas are the same ideas as expressed throughout these pages, only they are disguised a little differently each time. It is like seeing an old friend with different clothes on. Of course you recognise her; she doesn't have to wear the same clothes all the time for you to see who it is. The principle here is the same. It is the old adage, "as above, so below"; exactly the same laws apply whether you peer through a microscope or a telescope. The sun is an atom; an atom is a sun – it radiates. There are creatures in our garden who will be born, multiply and die in the time it takes for you to walk from one end to the other. To them you are a permanent feature. All of physical reality is constructed to the same laws, and is subject to them.

Medical science in conformity to our culture displays the habit of separating and labelling in a most complicated fashion a series of events which, if seen for what they are, form a whole.

Obscure disease labels are employed, each purporting to have nothing to do with the others, when in truth each is dependent upon the one before for its manifestation. Thus a person's disease is really one disease as expressed by one individual and not a confusion of separate items. This accentuates the importance of taking down an accurate history of the person before us.

It is the unity of the universe which is so important to realise and pursue. It is separatism leading to conflict which has grown like a tumour in our minds, our hearts, and therefore in our society. We think that because we are right then everyone else must be wrong – and how dogmatically this is displayed in homœopathic circles! This immediately denies the basis upon which the whole science rests – individuality.

All life is a unity and the whole of the universe is engaged in one mighty thrust forwards. If you hurt another, you hurt an aspect of yourself, as you will feel the pain of it in the post mortem state, just as they felt it. This is to enable us to build in right feeling for future lives so that we may conduct ourselves with decency, consideration and honesty in our dealings with others. The old tendencies to make the same mistakes will still be there, for we must grow consciously, deciding each stage for ourselves as we live.

THE HEAVENS

Having discarded his physical and vital bodies man is conscious for a while in the same way as in sleep. The desire body now takes on the shape of the physical form, having previously been of an oval shape. After this period of unconsciousness, man awakens in the desire world. He may not be aware of what has happened to him, he may not know that he has died. He may attempt to go to work, experiencing the frustration of seeing another at his desk. He has no physical vehicle and therefore cannot manifest effectively in the physical realm.

The clairvoyant can observe many who are stuck in this way, some for a considerable length of time. However, this is not the case when he moves from the 'first heaven' which is in the desire world to the 'second heaven' in the region of concrete thought.

Here the desire body drops away from him. He enters a silent world where he is alone, aware of himself yet he cannot actively think. He is unafraid and his soul is filled with a great peace. This space is called 'the great silence'.

He then awakens to his natural home, heaven, the world of tone. Here he begins the work of improving his vehicles. The essence of his three bodies are incorporated into the three-fold spirit, making an improved mind and desire body, a better vital body and a physical body more suited to his future needs. All this, in as much as he has allowed it to be so through right living. Also future provision is made for an improved environment and opportunities in accordance with needs arising from the incarnation just completed. He will only be able to build in the amount of work he has done on himself and his vehicles.

The deliberate cultivation of observation, retentive memory, veneration of truth, together with discrimination, concentration and persistence – a striving to live up to our own ideals and express them in thought, feeling and activity – make this spiritualisation of the being possible. It is what we really know to be right and its expression in life that is important, not the personality's petty rancour of not letting the other person 'get away with it'.

Man may dwell here in his natural house for centuries, assimilating the harvest of his past life and preparing the physical conditions on earth most suited to the life to come. He must work the fruits of past life into the proposed conditions which will form the stage for the ego's next venture in the field of experience. This process is to be seen in the body, in the assimilation of past intake and its conversion into substances suited to activity not yet undertaken.

The archetypal models of earth are in the region of concrete thought and it is from the 'heaven' world that all the inhabitants work on these models, changing, modifying and refining them. They change the physical features of the earth. Over the millennia it is well known that the earth has changed considerably, under direction from this realm, and the higher intelligences working through them on climate, flora and fauna.

Man is also actively learning how to build a body which will provide a greater means of expression. Here again we see the same process but with different levels and disguises. What man plunders from the planet in order to fulfil his earthly ambitions and its corresponding consequences in his own body, may be likened to the manner in which he builds his vehicles of expression in the heaven world and the substances he employs for that purpose. The measure of pollution in the environment which we are at present becoming aware of and concerned about is merely a reflection of what we are doing to our own bodies or inner environment.

To understand the nature and essence of an activity on any level will assist in understanding it on any other. Likewise, to observe the behaviour in a certain theatre of activity, in one in which we are to assist, will reveal the pattern which runs through every area of operation regarding life and its contents. When this is properly understood (as applied to oneself also), all the excuses and justifications are of no value and merely contribute as part of the pattern.

So man grows from childhood through adolescence (the present stage), to responsible conscious accomplishment. The law is that man will learn to live in the body he builds for himself, limited only by his and its capability. In this way he discovers its shortcomings and is taught how to correct them. Where the essence of his former bodies is built in creates an opportunity for conscious building, ever bringing before him past experiences and a degree of understanding. So the more advanced man is – by learning the lessons of the earthly life – the earlier the stage at which he begins to build consciously and extend his area for original creative possibility. As he learns to build in the heaven world he must know that he learns to wield his vehicles in the physical world.

The three semi-circular canals located inside the ear, each one finely adjusted in one of the three dimensions of space, have much to do with the faculty of space perception; logical thought and mathematical ability are in proportion to the accuracy of adjustment of these canals. Musical ability is also dependent on these, plus an extreme delicacy of the fibres of corti.

Having completed these tasks of past life assimilation, of having altered his own earth to provide the right conditions for future experience, and having built a suitable body for this purpose of physical expression, and lastly resolved the mind to the essence which builds the threefold spirit; the naked individual spirit ascends into the higher region of the world of thought, the 'third heaven'. Here it is strengthened for its next descent into matter.

Before the spirit is once again crucified upon the cross of matter (birth), there is the panorama of the coming incarnation beginning with the womb and ending at the tomb; but only the principle events or outline of the life are contained within it. There is free-will as to the execution of events. It is through the act of birth and childhood that the memory is lost. Here is much of the seed of understanding between freedom and fate, the balance between liberty and necessity. It is only through the realisation of responsibility, conscious or otherwise, of the life's task, and the willingness to cooperate with it that we secure real freedom. In avoiding our own issues we may think we are free; this is but an illusion. We take the responsibility, the freedom is how we choose to do it. This free will is a faculty we learn to acquire, by the deliberate cultivation of the power of choice. Most people are irresolute and would prefer to sit on the fence or wait to see which way the wind blows before making a decision. What they actually do is wait until they are forced by circumstance, then there is no longer a choice. The world has moved on and they are not innovators but sheep following with the mass.

The formation of habits appropriate to the task need to be constantly reviewed and kept up to date, ensuring the weeds are removed – this process can be conscious or subconscious. The narrowness of the mind or the all-seeing greatness that embraces a universe of possibilities; we must choose which is our lot. Ignorance, inability, instability and a general ineptitude all limit one's ability to realise and use free will. Knowledge, skill, honesty, integrity – all increase the amount of free will. A lack of freedom and ability to wield it is a sign of backwardness in evolution, just as one's ability to choose, decide, and act to meet what is necessary are a measure of achievement in growth.

BIBLIOGRAPHY

Bailey, Alice A., Esoteric Psychology Volumes I-V,
(London: Lucis Press, 1922).

Blavatsky, H.P., Isis Unveiled,
(Pasadena, CA, USA: Theosophical University Press, 1877, 1972).

Burnett, James Compton, The Liver,
(Delhi, India: Jain).

Burnett, James Compton, Fifty Reasons for Being a Homœopath,
(Delhi, India: Jain).

Burnett, James Compton, The Spleen,
(Delhi, India: Jain).

Heindel, Max, The Rosicrucian Cosmo-Conception,
(Oceanside,CA,USA: The Rosicrucian Fellowship, 1909, 1974).

Pryse, James Morgan, The Restored New Testament,
(London: Watkins, 1914, 1971).